DAMAGED

SOMETHING TO SING ABOUT!

Nov. 12. 03

Dear Kory:

Hope you will use this book.

I bought it for you when I saw the wonderful selections.

"Enjoy!"

Love
Mamaw Ethel

SOMETHING TO SING ABOUT!

The Personal Choices of America's Folk Singers

COLLECTED AND ARRANGED BY

MILTON OKUN

THE MACMILLAN COMPANY

COLLIER-MACMILLAN LTD., LONDON

Copyright © 1968 by Milton Okun

All rights reserved. No part of this book may be reproduced or transmitted in any form or by any means, electronic or mechanical, including photocopying, recording or by any information storage and retrieval system, without permission in writing from the Publisher.

All of the arrangements of public domain songs are copyright © 1968 by Milton Okun and may not be reprinted in any form without permission. Milton Okun makes no copyright claim to the authorship of any of the songs in this book.

The Macmillan Company
Collier-Macmillan Canada Ltd., Toronto, Ontario

Printed in the United States of America

Designer: Ernst Reichl

FOR JENNIFER AND ANDREW

CONTENTS

INTRODUCTION

A COLLECTION of favorites says a great deal about the people who make the choices. This one also says something about the nature of the folk movement and the bottomless well of music in American folk song. The one thing that unites all the folk singers in this book is their love and feeling for traditional music. Although some of the participants are writers and some are singers who rarely sing traditional material, it is the love and understanding of folk music that have been the major factors in the development of their art.

The folk revival has been considerably more than a musical phenomenon, much broader and more sweeping than a cultural event or an aspect of show-business development. America in general and American youth in particular began to rediscover itself through the vehicle of folk song. Because the music is so integrally tied in with our history, our sociology, our "feelings" as a people, the rediscovery of the music meant a discovery of the non-musical things that came along with the music. The impact of the folk revival of the Fifties created a new revolution in American pop music.

Folk singers boast of a meaningful credo. "We have," they say in one or another form, "something to sing about." This folk idiom is related to life, whether happy and optimistic or blue and ominous; life plays the harmony to folk melody. The rock 'n' roll of today has a shape and a substance and a lyrical content that it would never have had without this folk revival.

That, as much as anything, is what tradition is about. Tradition is the link to the past, the thread of history, the handclasp with the ancestor we never met. It is a form of immortality because it carries something forward from the long-distant past.

The discoveries and rediscoveries of the folk movement are still with us because of tradition. Even though folk music was temporarily upstaged by pop and rock music in 1965, the values and style of the folk movement simply extended into the new form of musical expression.

All of this is by way of showing that tradition need not be narrow or doctrinaire. Tradition tells us where we've been and thus helps show us where we *might* go, not where we *have* to go. Unfortunately, we have had more than a few spokesmen in folk song who lost their concepts of freedom when it came to the aesthetics of folk song. These generally libertarian people suddenly became rather narrow-minded about how a traditional song should be performed, how it should sound, what sort of accompaniment it deserves. The rule-setters didn't last long, because the singers, professional or back-porch variety, simply took over and ignored the rule-setters.

Now to the songs themselves. I asked each of the artists to choose a song that was either a favorite or one that was important or influential in the direction of their musical lives. Some of the choices were understandably from the singer's own repertoire, while a good many were songs admired from the repertoire of others. Inevitably there were some duplications. It's amazing that there weren't more. The first choice of both Josh White and Muddy Waters was "Things About Goin' My Way." Both Earl Robinson and Johnny Cash chose "John Henry." Sylvia Fricker and Judy Collins chose the twin variants "Greenwood Sidey-O" and "The Cruel Mother." There was a similar duplication of "Wagoner Lad" from the one Bob Gibson and the many Serendipity Singers. It seems especially interesting that the performers who chose the same selections are generally in the same age category. Where there was such a duplication, a second choice was used for one of the artists, either the second one heard from or the one who originally sent several alternates.

A basic problem in a book of folk songs that is meant to be used for singing is which particular version or variant of a song should be picked. Here the responsibility and choice were mine. The choices were not based on scholarly grounds. These songs are neither definitive versions nor authentic ones collected in the field but rather versions that are singable and those that lend themselves to interesting piano arrangements. In some cases the melodies are composites, in some cases the lyrics are. For better or worse, there are not too many folk-song purists in our collection, nor indeed are there many purists still around. Somehow it seems that everyone was concerned with getting to the heart of the music and to the life-experience that had gone into it. It was never the style of the American folk revival to spend a great deal of time on scholarly debates about authenticity.

Instead, it seems to me, what most of us have been concerned with has been the authenticity of real people, of real emotion, of true statement in the music. We didn't overly concern ourselves about the style of the Kingston Trio's "Tom Dooley" as much as we were concerned that the song told us something about a fragment of life in a portion of America in a slice of time remembered. That was what the folk revival was about, is about and will probably always be about—people and how they related to themselves, their feelings and the world through the ages. So, if a test for scholarly authenticity is needed, we'll fail the test, but we hope we pass when it deals with the authenticity of belief.

Incidentally, you may notice that in some songs the chords indicated for guitar are not the same as the chords to be played on the piano. I tried to write musically interesting piano arrangements that would be appealing when played alone as well as when used as accompaniment to singing. Sometimes this called for the use of chords or passing tones or bass lines that are awkward for guitar. In such instances the guitar chords indicated differ from the notes written for piano. However, all the songs are written in keys that all guitar pickers can pick with ease. One song in the book, "The Day Is Past and Gone," chosen by Jean Ritchie, does not have guitar chords. I believe the piano arrangement is very effective, but it can't be "translated" to guitar. If you don't use the piano, sing the song *a cappella*.

I did not include a section on how to play the chords in the book. There are innumerable folios, instruction books that are available. Most of the guitar chords used are quite simple. If the reader has trouble with any of the more difficult ones just contact the author in his New York studio.

During the time this book was in preparation, two of the participants died—Mississippi John Hurt and Woody Guthrie. Before he died, Mississippi John had given me his choice, but Woody's favorite was picked by his friend, Harold Leventhal.

Let's scan the roster to see how the singers made their choices. There is certainly no surprise to find that both Harry Belafonte and Theodore Bikel have chosen songs of the genre roughly called "protest," for both these singers have devoted lifetimes to social action.

Arlo Guthrie, who manages to sing clearly even with his tongue planted firmly in his cheek, had the cheek to include a classic of tradition that few folk singers ever touch, "Old McDonald Had a Farm."

Another new folk leader, Janis Ian, only recently a child herself, chose "God Bless' the Child." And perhaps it is surprising that as sophisticated and able a rural musician as Doc Watson would pick "Tom Dooley," although it may well illustrate the dual life of many folk musicians, whether sophisticated country or simplistic city.

Johnny Cash reveals his love of railroading by selecting "Rock Island Line," and Mahalia Jackson is true to her gospel tradition by including that classic of devotional songs "Balm in Gilead." Paul Robeson, one of the great voices of the past, echoes again for our time, choosing a song from our mutual past, "John Brown's Body."

I would like to thank several people for their help in preparing this collection: Harold Barlow, Harold Leventhal, Manuel Greenhill, Al Brackman, Robert Markel, Jean Goldhirsch, Arthur Mogull, the artists themselves and, on occasion, members of their families, their personal managers, all those upon whom we called time and again for various details—and especially my lovely sister-in-law, Jean Dinegar, who undertook the drudgery of coordination.

Something the entire folk world has learned from Pete Seeger is that there is a composer and a singer and an instrumentalist in all of us. Don't be afraid to try these piano arrangements, for I think you'll be pleasantly surprised at the results. And don't be afraid to try the guitar chordings or even to hum a melody line or two. A wonderful world of song is encapsulated in this collection of music, and a wonderful chorus of singers stands poised to tell you about themselves and the music they chose. I hope you enjoy this book as much as I did assembling it for you.

MILTON OKUN

SOMETHING
TO SING ABOUT!

WOODY GUTHRIE

CARLYLE'S famous essay on "Heroes and Hero Worship" was written quite a few years before the American folk revival. He might have been nonplussed had he been around to consider the enormous impact on two generations of Woodrow Wilson Guthrie.

Nothing seemed very heroic about this small, restless figure. But his work, his writings, his songs, his traveling, hard times and lingering death were the stuff of a hero.

Woody Guthrie didn't do his writing from a comfortable distance. He was one of the most involved writers who ever lived. His commitments and his artistic criticisms make him symbolic of a rich period in American history, a time of Depression, migratory workers, the Dust Bowl, natural conservation, labor organizing, patriotism, World War II. Woody Guthrie was to be a chronicler of a series of national upheavals, in the old troubadour tradition, writing of our nation in his 1,000 songs and thousands of still unpublished manuscript pages.

Woody Guthrie's story is being told by an increasing number of people, as a younger generation wonders who Woody Guthrie was and what he stood for. The story is being retold by singers and writers and all the people who had contact with Woody or his son, Arlo, or his widow, Marjorie.

The songs of Woody Guthrie represent some of the finest and most familiar works in American folk music. "This Land Is Your Land" has been called our national folk anthem. "So Long, It's Been Good to Know You" has become a parting song on a par with "Auld Lang Syne." His "Pastures of Plenty" and "Great Historical Bum" evoke the epic sweep of the American land and character. His children's songs are among the finest ever written, alive with humor and fantasy.

Woody's direct influence on Pete Seeger and Alan Lomax was as strong a shaping force on folk music as that of any singer save Leadbelly. Moe Asch built his record career on Guthrie, and other labels were keen to record what they could. The line of singers directly influenced would circle the globe—Jack Elliott, Bob Dylan, Woody's son, Arlo—countless dozens of others who adopted, if not the style, certainly the humanism core that characterized Guthrie.

His contribution is inestimable. His life was all too short, and a tragic illness made the last thirteen of his fifty-five years painful and unproductive. Even a year after his death, on October 4, 1967, Woody Guthrie still has not been fully revealed to the American people. Less than 20 percent of his writing has been published and only about 30 percent of his songs are widely known. *Bound for Glory*, a film about his life, is being produced by Harold Leventhal. Eventually, the American people will know the genius of Woody Guthrie.

17

Pretty Boy Floyd

By Woody Guthrie
Copyright © 1961 by Fall River Music Inc.
All rights reserved. Used by permission.

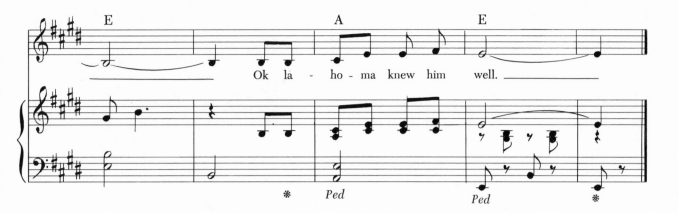

Ok la - ho - ma knew him well. _____

2 It was in the town of Shawnee,
It was Saturday afternoon,
His wife beside him in the wagon
As into town they rode.

3 There a deputy Sheriff approached him,
In a manner rather rude,
Using vulgar words of language,
And his wife she overheard.

4 Pretty Boy grabbed a log chain,
And the deputy grabbed a gun,
And in the fight that followed
He laid that deputy down.

5 He took to the trees and timbers,
And he lived a life of shame,
Every crime in Oklahoma
Was added to his name.

6 Yes, he took to the trees and timbers,
On that Canadian River's shore,
And Pretty Boy found a welcome
At many a farmer's door.

7 There's many a starvin' farmer,
The same old story told,
How this outlaw paid their mortgage,
And saved their little home.

8 Others tell you 'bout a stranger,
That come to beg a meal,
And underneath his napkin
Left a thousand dollar bill.

9 It was in Oklahoma City
It was on Christmas Day,
There came a whole car load of groceries,
With a letter that did say.

10 "You say that I'm an outlaw,
You say that I'm a thief,
Here's a Christmas dinner
For the families on relief."

11 Now as through this world I ramble,
I see lots of funny men,
Some will rob you with a six-gun,
And some with a fountain pen.

12 But as through this life you travel,
As through your life you roam,
You won't never see an outlaw,
Drive a family from their home.

Standing: Maybelle and A.P.
Seated: Sarah

THE CARTER FAMILY

The Carter Family, 1939 Seated: Helen, Anita, June; standing: A.P., Jeanette, "Brother Bill" (announcer XERA, Del Rio, Texas), Sarah, Maybelle

"WILDWOOD FLOWER," "Can the Circle Be Unbroken," "Worried Man Blues," "Keep on the Sunny Side" are but a few of the songs associated with the Carter Family, who may well be America's first family of folk song.

Scarcely an urban folk singer and probably no country singer of the last three decades has not drawn in some measure from the repertoire or manner of the Carter Family. The family trio from Maces Springs, Virginia, along with the late Jimmie Rodgers, stood as seminal performers who took traditional music and helped convert it into a whole catalogue of popular music.

A. P. Carter married Sara Dougherty in 1915. When joined in 1926 by Sara's cousin, Maybelle Addington, who was married to A. P. Carter's brother, the original Carter Family was formed. After an historic meeting in 1927 with the recording scout Ralph Peer, the trio went on to record more than 250 songs in the next 17 years, records that sold millions of copies despite the Depression.

The sound of the Carters was so homelike, so close to the best of American family singing that they held a special place in the American rural home. Whether they did sentimental parlor songs or gospel hymns or bright and cheerful ditties, the Carters rang true. Among their chief innovations was the addition of autoharp and guitar to traditional ballads that had always been unaccompanied. The famous and distinctive guitar playing of Mother Maybelle was

another innovation, a variation of the "church lick" that came to be called "Carter Family style."

During the years of World War II the Carter Family included the children of Sara and A. P.—Gladys, Jeannette and Joe—and what is considered the Carter Family today: Maybelle's children, Helen, June and Anita. A. P. Carter died in 1960, and Sara went into retirement, but Mother Maybelle continued to work with her three charming daughters.

Mother Maybelle has been lionized by the modern folk audience as much as she has been revered by the lovers of old-time country music. Whatever the gulf that stands between the folk-festival world of Newport and the country-music world of Nashville is bridged by the work of Mother Maybelle.

In both its early recordings and its latter-day performances, the Carter Family is at the vortex of home-made music. Although they turned professional and worked with the disciplines and pressures that professionalism demands, the Carter Family never lost its sense of purpose in music, its sense of faithfulness to a style and to conveying emotion through music. That their songs have been so widely performed is only one indication of the influence they have had on the listening and performing community. There is even one group—from Kentucky, the Phipps Family—that has built its entire career on the rock of Carter Family style.

For all the romanticism of the American folk movement, the Carter Family was a special symbol of another era, an era when families stayed together, prayed together and, above all, sang together. If for no other reason than that, the Carter Family has a claim to immortality that few can match.

The current group. Standing: Mother Maybelle, Anita, Helen; seated: June

Mollie Darling

Slowly, Smoothly

VERSE:

Won't you tell me, Mol-lie dar - ling, That you love none else but me? For I love you, Mol - lie dar - ling, You are all the world to me. Oh! Tell me, dar - ling that you love me, Put your lit - tle hand in mine.

22

2   Stars are smiling, Mollie darling,
Through the mystic vail of night;
They seem laughing, Mollie darling,
While fair Luna hides her light.
Oh! No one listens but the flowers,
While they hang their heads in shame,
They are modest, Mollie darling,
When they hear me call your name.

CHOICE OF THE CARTER FAMILY

Johnny, I Hardly Knew You

2 I'm happy for to see you home, haruh, haruh,
I'm happy for to see you home, haruh, haruh,
I'm happy for to see you home, but oh my darling so pale and wan,
So low in cheek, so high in bone,
Oh Johnny I hardly knew you.

3 Where are your legs that used to run, haruh, haruh,
Where are your legs that used to run, haruh, haruh,
Where are your legs that used to run when first you went to carry a gun?
Indeed your dancing days are done,
Oh Johnny I hardly knew you.

4 Where are your eyes that were so mild, haruh, haruh,
Where are your eyes that were so mild, haruh, haruh,
Where are your eyes that were so mild when first my heart you so
    beguiled?
Oh, why did you run from me and the child?
Oh Johnny I hardly knew you.

5 You haven't an arm, you haven't a leg, haruh, haruh,
You haven't an arm, you haven't a leg, haruh, haruh,
You haven't an arm, you haven't a leg, you're an eyeless,
    boneless, chickenless egg
And you'll have to be put in a bowl to beg.
Oh Johnny I hardly knew you.

6 (Repeat 1st verse)

CHOICE OF THE CARTER FAMILY

Come All Ye Fair and Tender Ladies

Moderately

Come all ye fair _____ and ten-der lad-ies, _____ Take warn-ing
how _____ you court young men; _____ They're like a star _____ on a sum-mer's

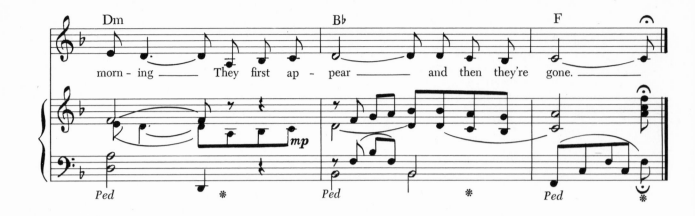

morn - ing ___ They first ap - pear ___ and then they're gone. ___

2 They'll tell to you some flattering story,
   And swear to God that they love you well,
And away they'll go and court some other,
   And leave you here in grief to dwell.

3 I wish I was in some tall mountain,
   Where the ivy rock is black as ink;
I would write a letter to my false lover,
   Whose cheeks are like the morning pink.

4 I wish I was some little sparrow,
   And one of them that could fly so high;
I would fly away to my true love's dwelling,
   And when he would speak I would be close by.

5 But I am none of those little sparrows,
   Or none of those that fly so high,
So I'll sit down in grief and sorrow,
   And pass all my troubles by.

CHOICE OF THE CARTER FAMILY

Wildwood Flower

Moderate—Country Style

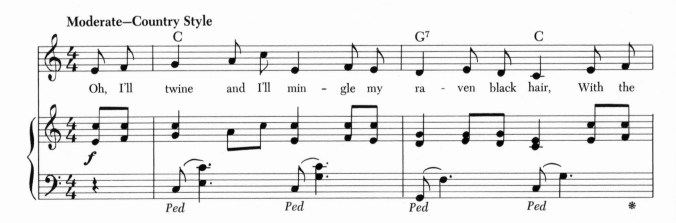

Oh, I'll twine and I'll min - gle my ra - ven black hair, With the

2 He taught me to love him; he promised to love,
To cherish me always all others above.
Another has won him, I'm sorry to tell.
He left me no warning, no words of farewell.

3 How I weep to remember he called me his flower,
And he said that I cheered him through life's dreary hour,
All these soft words aside, I could hardly have known
That his pale wildwood flower would be left all alone.

MISSISSIPPI
JOHN HURT

A CURIOUS thing happened during the heat of the folk revival. Certain formerly obscure musicians, to whom music had been more a personal expression than a professional way of life, were catapulted to national fame, becoming, for want of a better phrase, "ethnic stars."

One such ethnic star was Mississippi John Hurt. The sense of personal loss so many of us felt at his death in 1966 was one measure of how close he became to all who had had any contact with him.

John Hurt was a most amazing man and musician. The septuagenarian former field hand and cattle herdsman radiated a peace and a warmth that affected everyone. The face of John Hurt, creased with age and care and broad smiles, was a favorite of photographers. The very look of him seemed to reveal what a good part of this folk-music revival was all about—the speaking through music of the self-taught musician.

John Hurt came from the Mississippi Delta, yet his music was unlike the hard, biting blues of other Delta musicians. Rather it was a sort of folk chamber music, in which one man and his guitar could orchestrate a whole range of emotions. He compelled our attention by his understatement, by his playful wit, his craftsmanship and his gentle voice.

The name of John Hurt went far beyond the folk audience in 1963 and 1964 in major articles in *Time, Newsweek, The New York Times.* The contrasts and

the sudden fame were irresistible to feature writers. They marveled at how, in six months, he jumped from $28 a month wages on a farm at Avalon, Mississippi, to more than $300 a week in the folk club circuit. The sharecropper who had seventeen grandchildren had been lost to the world since some 1928 recordings on the Okeh label. Tom Hoskins, a Washington record and music buff, traced John back to Avalon and recorded him on the Piedmont label.

Soon John Hurt was appearing at Newport, on the "Tonight" Show, at Carnegie and Town Halls and folk festivals around the continent. His first guitar, "Black Annie," had cost his mother $1.50, but the Newport Foundation replaced that with an instrument worthy of his skill. His shoulders hunched, his head half hidden in a spotted old brown hat, John became a symbol of the rediscovery of native folk artists.

One of his songs provided the inspiration for the pop group, the Lovin' Spoonful, and other songs entered just about everyone's repertory. John brought something musical and human to every place he played. The tragedy was that thirty five years intervened between his first recordings and the fame that marked the last years of his life.

The wry confection called "Candy Man" was John's choice for this book. It is typical of the man's gentle legacy to us of music filled with wit and warmth.

Candy Man Blues

Moderate Blues

Well, all you la-dies gath-er round,__ The good sweet can-dy man's in town.__ It's the can-dy man,__ can-dy man.__

Words and music by John Hurt
Copyright © 1963 by Wynwood Music Co.
Used by permission.

2 He's got a stick of candy nine-inch long,
He sells it as fast as a hog can chew corn,
It's the candy man, candy man.

3 You all heard what Sister Jones has said,
Always takes a candy stick to bed,
It's the candy man, candy man.

4   Don't stand close to the candy man,
He'll leave a candy stick in your hand,
It's the candy man, candy man.

5   He sold some candy to Sister Bad,
The very next day, she took all he had,
It's the candy man, candy man.

6   If you try his candy, good friend of mine,
You sure will want it for a long, long time,
It's the candy man, candy man.

7   His stick candy don't melt away,
Just gets better so the ladies say,
It's the candy man, candy man.

PAUL ROBESON

HOW SAD that time and illness have prevented a whole generation of Americans from knowing about that magnificent artist and person, Paul Robeson. This fabled Negro singer and leader has been in semi-retirement for years now, yet his figure still looms large in the worlds of music and of civil rights.

To an earlier generation, the towering presence of Paul Robeson was as strong as the late Reverend Dr. Martin Luther King, Jr. While their methods or tactics or philosophies may have differed, their ultimate aims did not—the achievement of total emancipation, of first-class citizenship and dignity for all Negro Americans and, in fact, for all poor or oppressed Americans.

Robeson was born in 1898 in Princeton, New Jersey, son of an escaped slave who became a minister. The son's long and distinguished career of personal and objective honors began at Rutgers University, from which he graduated with high standing and where he was a football star, later an All-American end. He obtained a law degree from Columbia, but his interest in theater soon supplanted these academic pursuits.

His first stage triumphs were in a series of O'Neill plays and in Shakespeare's *Othello*. Soon he was singing, and his big and lustrous bass-baritone overwhelmed all who heard it. At first he established himself by singing spirituals, but then he became deeply involved with an heroic cantata, "Ballad for Americans," that was to stand as a great achievement for all connected with the work, including the singer Paul Robeson. (See Earl Robinson on page 77 for more about "Ballad for Americans.")

During the early 1940s Paul Robeson enjoyed the special status that a wartime America could find for its Negro leaders. His recordings were widely popular and he was a concert star of great proportions. This reached a turning point, however, when postwar tensions and suspicions crystallized at the Peekskill riots of June 1949 when Westchester County rightists and veteran's groups organized a tragic episode of rock-throwing violence against Robeson and a group of Negroes, Jews and progressives.

After Peekskill, Robeson and many another great figure fell under the dark shadow of McCarthyism. As the journalist Martha Dodd has written: "Peekskill was also a turning point in Paul Robeson's career. He became, thereafter, a prisoner in his native land. For nearly a decade he suffered an economic, cultural, political and often even personal boycott of formidable proportions. His means of livelihood was drastically reduced, his musical recordings banned, his passport denied, his name 'scandalized' and obscenely reviled, his achievements wiped off the official slate of American history...."

Now that bad period has passed, although those who lived with it or watched Robeson live through it thought the night would never pass. But Robeson was left ill and hurt. Somehow his stature of the old days would never be recaptured, or, if not "never," then "not yet." Robeson was a phenomenon—a distinguished Negro who fought back, who never said he would take what white America or especially what reactionary white America had to dish out to a strong individual like him. Modestly, Robeson has described himself as a folk singer. In the larger, classic sense of the term, he is a folk singer of the strong and universal type we all revere.

31

John Brown's Body

Strong and Moderately Fast

VERSE:

John Brown's bod-y lies a-mould-'ring in the grave,

John Brown's bod-y lies a-mould-'ring in the grave,

John Brown's bod-y lies a-mould-'ring in the grave, But his

2 The stars of Heaven are looking kindly down,
The stars of Heaven are looking kindly down,
The stars of Heaven are looking kindly down,
On the grave of old John Brown.

3 He's gone to be a soldier in the army of the Lord!
He's gone to be a soldier in the army of the Lord!
He's gone to be a soldier in the army of the Lord!
His soul is marching on.

THERE IS an other-world quality about the songs of John Jacob Niles and an other-era quality about his performing manner. The man who has been called the "dean of American balladeers" has lived through so many folk revivals that perhaps only Charles Seeger, the musicologist, and the late Carl Sandburg had seen more flux and change in American folk song.

Niles is a curious anomaly. He is a trained singer, resident in Kentucky. He is a man of general culture who has stayed close to the soil and still farms. He sings in a style that is both simple and sophisticated.

A few of the songs written by John Jacob Niles are classics of the folk idiom—"Black Is the Color of My True Love's Hair," "Go 'Way from My Window" and "I Wonder as I Wander" are among the most well known of his many compositions. He also was the key figure in popularizing the eight-string dulcimer as an accompanying instrument.

Niles was born in 1892 in Louisville, Kentucky, grew up near there and lives today in Clark County, Kentucky. His family was peppered with singers and storytellers. John Jacob was a serious student of classical piano and attended the Cincinnati Conservatory of Music, the University and Conservatory of Music at Lyons and the Schola Cantorum in Paris.

His long career as a collector started when he was only fifteen and continued right through his service with the Air Corps in World War I. During the war he gathered material of Negro soldiers and a general collection of Army songs called "Songs My Mother Never Taught Me."

His collecting has ranged wide and deep throughout the Southern mountains. At one time he remarked: "Only twice in thirty-six years of folklore collecting have I resorted to paying money for the privilege of taking down a folk song, though I must admit chewing tobacco, whiskey, bacon, fat-back, lard, string, cotton gloves, cornmeal, wheat-flower, almanacs, corn-cob pipes, aspirin, soda and other blandishments too numerous to mention, are polite bribes."

When Niles sings, it is a unique experience. The face, beneath the gray hair, is serene; the dulcimer strings are most gentle. His tenor voice often soars into an eerie falsetto that is almost chilling. It is a trade-mark and one of the few unimitated voices in all American folk song.

John Jacob Niles has published hundreds of fine musical arrangements under the imprint of Schirmer and Fischer. These have been widely used by solo singers and college choruses over the years. He has also written a variety of lengthy, more ambitious works, including the oratorio "Lamentation," "Rhapsody for the Merry Month of May" and a Christmas cantata, "Mary the Rose."

Many of the younger people in the current folk revival know of John Jacob Niles only by name, although he has several LP recordings on several labels. His concerts have been few in recent years, but his firm and unusual voice has weathered the years remarkably well. Niles is of another age, and yet he has contributed so much to our own that he deserves more attention than he has received. As one of the deans of the folk-music movement, he was among the first to build a career from the art of traditional music.

JOHN JACOB NILES

Barbary Ellen

In Scar-let Town where I was born, There was a fair maid dwell-ing, Made ev'-ry youth cry — "well-a-day." Her name was Bar - b'ry El - len.

John Jacob Niles
Copyright 1936 by G. Schirmer, Inc.
in "More Songs of the Hill-Folk"

2 'Twas in the merry month of May,
When the green buds they were swelling,
Sweet William on his death-bed lay,
For the love of Barbary Ellen.

3 He sent his servant to the town,
To the place where she was dwelling,
Said, "Master bids you come to him,
If your name be Barbary Ellen."

35

4 Then slowly slowly got she up,
And slowly went she nigh him,
And as she drew the curtains back—
"Young man, I think you're dying."

5 "Oh yes, I'm sick, I'm very sick,
And I never will be better,
Until I have the love of one—
The love of Barbary Ellen."

6 "Oh ken ye not in yonders town,
In the place where ye were dwelling,
Ye gave a health to the ladies all,
But ye slighted Barbary Ellen."

7 "Oh yes, I ken, I ken it well,
In the place where I was dwelling,
I gave a health to the ladies all,
But my love to Barbary Ellen."

8 Then lightly tripped she down the stair,
He trembled like an aspen—
" 'Tis vain, 'tis vain, my dear young man,
To hone for Barbary Ellen."

9 He turned his pale face to the wall,
For death was in him dwelling—
"Goodbye, kind friends and kin-folk all,
Be kind to Barbary Ellen."

10 As she did pass the wooded fields,
She heard his death bell knelling,
And every stroke hit spoke her name,
"Hard-hearted Barbary Ellen."

11 Her eyes looked east, her eyes looked west,
She saw his pale corpse coming,
"O bearers, bearers, put him down,
For I am now a-dying."

12 "O mother dear, go make my bed,
Go make it soft and narrow;
Sweet William died for love of me,
And I will die for sorrow."

13 "O father dear, go dig my grave,
Go dig it deep and narrow;
Sweet William died for love of me,
And I will die for sorrow."

14 They buried her in the old churchyard,
Sweet William's grave was nigh her,
And from his heart grew a red, red rose,
And from her heart a briar.

15 They grew themselves to the old church wall,
Twill they couldn't grow no higher;
They grew twill they tied a true-lovers' knot,
The red rose round the briar.

MUDDY WATERS

THE NOTED performers who go through periods of early fame and then on to later developments are always fascinating. The Maurice Chevaliers and Rudy Vallees are entertainment-world legends.

But consider the double life of Muddy Waters. His first "career" was in the early years of World War II when he was recorded for the Archive of American Folk Song. Then he was a Mississippi field hand, one of the great Delta blues men with a rough yet stunning voice. Today, in the full sweep of his second career, he is a Chicago blues man, running a gutsy band on the South Side of Chicago. His style has changed and so has the man.

Between these two extremes lies one of the most fascinating stories in American folk and popular music. For the folk purist, of whom there are still all too many around, Muddy Waters—or McKinley Morganfield, as he was formally named—should never have left the miserable Delta if it was a question of keeping his music close to the soil. For those with more compassion, the upward route of Muddy Waters was inevitable as the change in his music.

But even this estimation does not take into account the fact that Muddy can still play both his earlier folk-based blues and the pungent, more sophisticated big-city blues. At several folk festivals, including Newport, Muddy and his band have done just that—played his early style and his later style, and they are two aspects of an unresolved question about change and growth and differentiation in musical style.

It would be impossible, if not insulting, to try to summarize this epic evolution of a Negro plantation cottonfield worker to a show-business luminary in the Negro ghetto of Chicago in only a few paragraphs. Rather, let us recommend that you try to follow that change yourself in several excellent books and through recordings.

Particularly effective for their general value in showing the poetic pulse of the blues and their sociological overtones are Paul Oliver's two masterly works, *Blues Fell This Morning* and *Conversation with the Blues*, both of which deal in detail with Muddy Waters. Also recommended is Pete Welding's private reissue of *Muddy Waters: Down on Stovall's Plantation* (Testament Records T-2210), taken from recordings made by Alan Lomax and John Work for the Library of Congress. The later Muddy Waters can be heard with his Chicago band on the Chess label.

Consider, then, this metamorphosis, from the direst of poverty and the life of imprisoned sorrow that is Negro country blues into the lively world of Chicago blues that has had such an enormous impact upon the entire popular music world. Muddy Waters made that journey gracefully and with musical artistry as a bluesman, first and foremost. It is one we should all study and learn to evaluate. There was nothing musically more superior in the beginnings of that journey than in its end; there is only a difference. If the music changes as the man's life improves, let us not carry our fascination with purist style to the point of wanting to freeze men into attitudes of sorrow and poverty to perpetuate that style.

Things About Goin' My Way

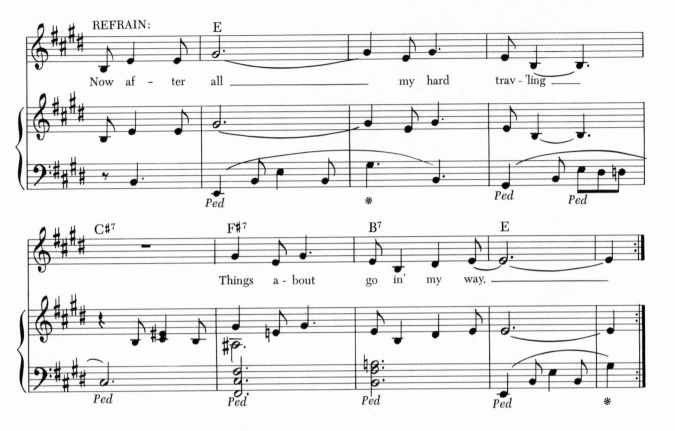

2 The pot was empty,
The cupboard bare,
I said, "Mama, Mama,
What's going on here?"

3 The rent was due,
The light was out,
I said, "Mama, Mama
What's it all about?"

4 Mama told me,
"Sickness got me down.
If you won't work
I'm gonna leave this town."

5 I work like a slave,
Don't get no rest,
To keep the woman
That I love the best.

tenant farmers of English-Irish descent. Being of a singing family, he was hurtled on stage at the age of four, singing some fifteen verses of "Barbara Allen" for an audience. In 1929 he left Eastern Illinois State Teachers College to begin part of his life as a "wayfaring stranger," the song title that he was later to use as a title for his autobiography.

Ives went on the road a few years after Carl Sandburg, a few years before Woody Guthrie and Pete Seeger—the late 1920s and early 1930s were the incubation and exploration period for that generation of American folk singers. It was a colorful and romantic period: For Burl Ives, his singing of "The Foggy Dew" in a Utah town landed him in jail.

In the late 1930s he landed in New York and began his dual career as actor and folk singer. From a bit part in *The Boys from Syracuse* he moved to other shows and in 1940 began his national radio show, "The Wayfaring Stranger." After Army service, he appeared in the Broadway smash *Sing Out, Sweet Land* and soon he was most actively sought for nightclub and concert appearances.

A very active recording career was followed by such straight dramatic roles as in *Cat on a Hot Tin Roof* and then a subsidiary career as a film star began. Musically, Ives was to waver a bit, despite the enormity of his established recorded library, and made some records in a watered-down Nashville style that were popular but added little to his stature.

Despite the length and breadth of his many careers, Burl Ives left an indelible stamp upon the face of American folk music. Some ascribe his latter-day detachment from the folk movement to distaste for some of the left-wing elements of the movement. Perhaps it boils down to an Ives belief that "he travels farthest who travels alone." It is the early recordings, collections and writings of Burl Ives that are the greatest adornment of his career. In the great democratic upsurge in America during the World War II era, he was there giving it folk substance and folk melody. Although his disassociation from the folk world in the last decade has been a loss to him and the world, one must remain indebted to Ives for his great influence on American folk song.

O NE OF the inescapable mysteries of the folk boom of the 1960s has been how one of the undisputed parents of the revival, Burl Ives, managed to keep himself so completely distant from his progeny. The answer must lie with Ives himself, for on many occasions the young enthusiasts and fans who had been so influenced by him tried to close the gap, but without success.

Whatever the direct contact with Ives had been, his influence was certainly enormous. A whole generation, in the 1940s and 1950s, had developed many of its ideas about folk repertory and performance from the recordings of Ives. Besides having the true country feeling in his early recordings, Ives captured the quality of the relaxed storyteller in song.

Burl Ives was born to a large family of Illinois

BURL IVES

Johnny Doolan's Cat

By Burl Ives
Copyright © 1963 by Wayfarer Music Inc., New York, N.Y.
Used by permission. All rights reserved.

JOSH WHITE

ALTHOUGH ancestor-worship is rooted in world folklore, the young folk revivalists of the 1960s tended, all too often, to negate or ignore the past. Among the pillars of the past who has never gotten the honors he deserves was Josh White.

Josh White perhaps more than any single performer brought folk songs and blues to the American

cabaret audience. In a time of great democratic upsurge, during World War II, he was the closest we had to a national minstrel. Befriended by the Roosevelts, Josh held the ear of the White House as well as the ear of millions during the peak of his popularity.

Because of his rural Southern Negro roots and his musical and verbal articulateness, Josh White focused as much interest on the meaning of the blues as had almost any performer before him. Because he had witnessed lynchings, undergone deprivation and discrimination, Josh White could tell the emerging liberal-Left urban coalition what Negro life in the South was all about.

He told that story, in song and word, with the drama and intensity of a born performer. He did not have the rawness or force of a Leadbelly but was a sophisticate who could talk with identification to a white middle-class audience. Leadbelly was a phenomenon to many while Josh White was a person.

He was born in Greenville, South Carolina, to a preacher's family. Though the religious element was strongly imbedded in him, he chose to work with secular blues. His schooling was of the most stringent sort, on the streets and alleyways of the South, where, as a boy, he would lead blind Negro street singers along their paths. He made his way north to Chicago, then to New York, and in the 1930s he began recording both blues and religious songs, the latter under a variety of pseudonyms to avoid offending the pious.

It was his long runs at the Village Vanguard and his three years at the Cafe Society clubs that really established Josh as a major interpretive force. Dozens of blues and other songs were to become his trade-marks, among them "John Henry," "Scandalize My Name," "Jelly, Jelly," "One Meat Ball," "The Riddle Song," "Talkin' Names," "Jim Crow Train," "Told My Captain." The list is long and distinguished.

There was theatricality and artifice in the young Josh White. Year upon year of cabaret and concert performing honed these elements into the matured polish that has dominated his work for more than three decades. He uses his guitar with stunning effect, the answering, complementing string voice stinging and underlining his own voice. He was, and is, a master of phrasing, arching long and intense lines into songs that he does with new vitality in each performance.

Josh White is still a force in American folk song. When he props his foot onto a chair to support his guitar, when he mops his sweaty brow, when he dips into light bawdry or into impassioned musical plaints, he becomes the total personality of the Negro minstrel.

The Riddle Song

gave my love a ba - by with no cry - in'.

2   How can there be a cherry that has no stone?
How can there be a chicken that has no bone?
How can there be a story that has no end?
How can there be a baby with no cryin'?

3   A cherry, when it's blooming, it has no stone.
A chicken when it's pippin', it has no bone.
The story of "I love you," it has no end.
A baby when it's sleeping, is no cryin'.

For MANY reasons the American folk audience has been painstakingly selective about the Country and Western performers it admires. All the more honor to such important figures as Johnny Cash and Merle Travis that they are equally accepted by the Nashville audience and the Newport fans.

Merle Travis is an important figure on several scores—as a guitar giant, as a first-rate songwriter, as a compelling singer and as one of the intellectuals of country music.

As a guitar stylist Travis is of commanding interest. The method called Travis-picking can be described as a three-finger picking style using thumb and first and second fingers. The thumb plays the bass notes while the other fingers take the melody either on or off the beat. The vitality and interest of the style is achieved as much by the omission of certain upbeats as well as by their stress.

Merle's style can be traced back to a Negro Kentuckian, Jim Mason, who taught his "choke" style of guitar to Mose Reger, a white coal miner, and to Ike Everly, father of the Everly brothers. Travis learned it from Reger and later was to be a "great influence" on Chet Atkins.

Travis is reputed to have designed and to help build the first flat-top guitar, which has since become

MERLE TRAVIS

a standard in guitar manufacture. In his hands it is one of the finest guitar articulations in country—or folk—music.

To the popular listener, however, it was the wonderful country songs of Merle Travis that established his strong reputation.

Many of these songs have since become standards: "Sweet Temptation," "Cincinnati Lou," "So Round, So Firm, So Fully Packed," "Dark as a Dungeon" and "Smoke, Smoke, Smoke." Merle's master work, "Sixteen Tons," became one of the major popular hits of this century after its recording by Tennessee Ernie Ford, and it is still used by that singer as a signature tune.

In his songs of the coal-miners Travis is reflecting his actual familiarity with the life and hard times of Kentucky miners, having had many of them in his own family. But he had an ear for pop taste as well and could take these realistic laments and protests and give them an articulate form that carried them far from the Kentucky coal mines.

Travis played for a time in his early days with the old string band Pappy McMichen and His Georgia Wildcats before going on to solo work. After serving in the Marines he moved to the West Coast, where he now makes his home.

Travis is very active with the John Edwards Memorial Foundation at the University of California at Los Angeles. This research center is striving to make country music known and appreciated as the art form that it truly is. Travis has lent his name and prestige to the work of the foundation, but it is his own creative work that has done more to demonstrate the genuine folk roots in country music than any other activity.

47

Pretty Polly

2   "Pretty Polly, pretty Polly, come along with me,
Pretty Polly, pretty Polly, come along with me,
Before we get married some pleasure to see."

3   He led her over hills and the valley so deep,
He led her over hills and the valley so deep,
Until pretty Polly she started to weep.

4   He led her a little farther and what did they spy,
He led her a little farther and what did they spy
But a new-dug grave with a spade lying by.

5   "O Willy, O Willy, I'm afraid of your way,
O Willy, O Willy, I'm afraid of your way,
I'm afraid you will lead my poor body astray."

6   "Pretty Polly, pretty Polly, you guessed just about right,
Pretty Polly, pretty Polly, you guessed just about right,
I dug on your grave best part of last night."

7   She throw'd her arms around him and trembled with fear,
She throw'd her arms around him and trembled with fear.
"How can you kill a girl that was to you so dear?"

8   He stabbed her to the heart, her heart's blood it did flow,
He stabbed her to the heart, her heart's blood it did flow,
And into the grave pretty Polly did go.

9   He throw'd a little dirt over her and started for home,
He throw'd a little dirt over her and started for home,
Leaving nothing behind but the wild birds to moan.

REVEREND GARY DAVIS

FROM the time of Homer, if not before, the blind were forced by their disability into callings that relied on other skills and senses than their sight. In our own country and time, the streets have been populated by the sightless street singer, the itinerant minstrel who chose to sing rather than to beg.

This great tradition brought us such great, classic Negro performers as Blind Lemon Jefferson, Willie Johnson, Sonny Terry, Snooks Eaglin and Joe Taggart. It also brought us the Reverend Gary Davis, who uses not only this vibrant style of singing but also epitomizes the very best of a style called "holy blues."

A sharp delineation was made among the pious Southern Negroes between sacred music and "sinful" music. Often the singer of one form could never cross into the other realm for risk of offending his audience. Somehow, as the recorded work of the great Blind Willie Johnson will attest, a compromise form was achieved—in the use of "sinful" or secular music forms with sacred or devotional lyrics. And so it was that the holy blues men were among the very best of the practitioners of the blues although their message was quite contrary to the despairing, rough and rueful message of the blues.

Gary Davis was born in Lawrence County, South Carolina, and was immersed in music before he became totally blind in his thirties. About that time he also became a preacher and turned his full interest to gospel singing. He learned almost all of his material by ear, from live performances or phonograph records. He has composed a great deal of his own material and brings the fervor of the down-home preacher to his performances of such durable holy blues as "Twelve Gates to the City," "You've Got to Move," "I Can't Make the Journey by Myself." One song, "If I Had My Way," associated with Gary Davis was given national popularity by Peter, Paul and Mary.

The voice of Gary Davis is one of the rare and wondrous folk instruments of our time, a mahogany baritone that is often scratchy with wear and age and yet always with the luster of a great antique. His careening dynamics, his shouts, rasps, flutters and melancholy swoops have entranced young urban listeners as few country-born performers have.

As an equal partner in "his act," Reverend Davis works with a fine old guitar that is played with the best and most imaginative of techniques. At home in the Bronx, New York, Gary Davis won deep admiration as a teacher of guitar to scores of aspiring performers and many practicing professionals.

For a time the Reverend Gary Davis worked with the assistance of a talented young musician-composer-arranger, Barry Kornfeld, who first appeared with him at the first Newport Folk Festival of 1959. Kornfeld was the most committed of the many city folk fans who recognize the worth and the genius of Reverend Gary Davis. That Gary Davis has remained a musician's musician rather than mass-audience phenomenon is only a loss to that mass audience.

Twelve Gates to the City

Moderate—Strong

REFRAIN:

Oh, what a beau-ti-ful ci-ty! Oh, what a beau-ti-ful ci-ty! Oh, what a beau-ti-ful ci-ty! Twelve gates to the ci-ty, hal-le-lu-jah!

2 My Lord built that city,
He said it was four square;
He said He wanted you sinners
To meet Him in the air,
  'Cause He built
Twelve gates to the city, hallelujah!

THE WEAVERS

"IF IT were not for the work of the Weavers," the old Scots song muses. Those who love American folk song might make the same sort of comment, because it is difficult to imagine where American folk song would be if it were not for the work of the Weavers.

The quartet stands like a connecting link in a chain, between the root folk song of the 1930s and the urban revival of the 1950s and after. They helped translate the rough and rowdy music of our rural tradition into a music for the cabaret, for the concert hall and for radio and television. They helped promote the acceptance of international folk song as a true art, and used nothing but the most honest of methods to do it.

The name of the group was chosen to express work, rhythm and the sense of rural handicraft. The group was an outgrowth of an earlier urban-country aggregation called the Almanac Singers. To Pete Seeger, the reason for forming a pop-folk group was to find some way of bringing the massive musical statements of Leadbelly to more people. He felt no single person could handle that.

The first appearance of consequence was at the Village Vanguard at Christmas, 1949. The blessings of Carl Sandberg, Alan Lomax and Gordon Jenkins (an arranger and orchestra leader) were bestowed on the original foursome there and things began to look very good. The original Weavers were Pete Seeger, Lee Hays, Ronnie Gilbert and Fred Hellerman. All were steeped in traditional song. All were also sophisticated musicians who knew and believed that it was possible, in Lee's words, to be "good and commercial."

Soon the group's recordings on the Decca label were breaking through to the Hit Parade of 1950. Such bright and cheerful Weavers' arrangements as "Good Night, Irene," "On Top of Old Smoky," "Kisses Sweeter Than Wine" and "When the Saints Go Marching In" were to establish the quartet in the popular mind as folk singers par excellence.

After two of the palmiest years experienced by any folk group anywhere, the Weavers disbanded at the end of 1952. The reasons were twofold—personal and because of the anti-Leftist blacklist which had caused the group to lose many bookings. It was the worst period of McCarthyism, and the scourge of reaction led to terrible reprisals against anyone of left-of-center leanings, actual or suspected.

In 1955 Harold Leventhal, the Weavers' personal manager and producer, reactivated the group for an historic Christmas concert at Carnegie Hall. A new wave of popularity ensued, and they made international tours for several years. The group continued to record on the Vanguard label, and Pete Seeger was able to maintain a solo career while also working with the group. In 1958 the demands of his own work were so great that Pete retired from the group, and he was succeeded, successively, by Erik Darling, Frank Hamilton and, finally, Bernie Krause. By the end of 1963, after having marked a triumphant fifteen years with an anniversary concert series at Carnegie Hall, the group decided to disband. The rigors of traveling and the desire to pursue independent careers led to this end.

But it was not really an end for a group that had been such a force in shaping American pop-folk music. Somewhere, between the raspy harshness of tradition and the musicianly shaping of professional polish, the Weavers attained a vital sense of balance. That balance was to become a standard for all the pop-folk groups that followed. Ringing in their ears were the sounds of the recordings by the Weavers.

For this collection Fred Hellerman chose "I Ride an Old Paint," for many reasons, but mostly for the "real toughness and harsh reality of the cowboy's life." Ronnie Gilbert chose "The Dodger Song" because, "as life gets complexer this simple old folk song gets timelier." Lee Hays likes too many songs to pick just one.

Ronnie, Pete, Lee, Fred

I Ride an Old Paint

Moderately

VERSE:

I ride an old paint, _ I lead an old Dan, _ I'm goin' to Mon - ta - na to throw the Hoo - li - an. They feed in the cou - lees, They wa - ter in the draw, Their

tails are all mat - ted, Their backs are all raw.

REFRAIN: Ride a - round lit - tle do - gies Ride a - round ____ them _ slow, For the

fie - ry and snuff - y Are rar - ing to go.

2 Old Bill Jones had a daughter and a son
Son went to college and the daughter went wrong
His wife got killed in a pool-room fight
Still he keeps singing from morning till night.

3 When I die take my saddle from the wall
Put it on to my pony lead him out of his stall
Tie my bones to his back turn our faces to the west
And we'll ride the prairie that we love the best

4 I worked in the city, I worked on the farm;
All I got to show is the muscle on my arm.
Blisters on my feet and callous on my hands,
And I'm going to Montana to throw the Houlihan.

The Dodger Song

Yes, the can - di - date's a dodg - er Yes, a well known dodg - er, Yes, the

can - di - date's a dodg - er, Yes, and I'm a dodg - er too. He'll

meet you and treat you And ask you for your vote, But

look out, boys, — he's a - dodg - ing for a note.

REFRAIN:

Yes, we're all dodg - ing, Dodg - ing, dodg - ing, dodg - ing, Yes, we're

all dodg - ing our way through the world.

2 Oh, the lawyer he's a dodger,
yes, a well known dodger,
Oh, the lawyer he's a dodger,
yes, and I'm a dodger, too.
He'll plead your case and
claim you for a friend,
But look out, boys, he's easy
for to bend!

3   Oh, the merchant he's a dodger,
      yes, a well known dodger,
Oh, the merchant he's a dodger,
      yes, and I'm a dodger, too.
He'll sell you goods at double the price,
But when you go to pay him,
      you'll have to pay him twice!

4   Oh, the farmer he's a dodger,
      yes, a well known dodger,
Oh, the farmer he's a dodger,
      yes, and I'm a dodger, too.
He'll plow his cotton, he'll hoe his corn,
But he'll make a living just as sure as you're born!

5   Oh, the lover he's a dodger,
      yes, a well known dodger,
Oh, the lover he's a dodger,
      yes, and I'm a dodger too.
He'll hug you and kiss you, and call you his bride,
But look out, girls, he's telling you a lie!

PETE SEEGER

PETE SEEGER has been fighting a losing battle in the folk world for some years now, a remarkable fact for such a winning personality and performer. The battle he continually loses is the one he wages against "the star system," "personality cults" or "the leadership syndrome." We all listen to his great ideas against such potentially dangerous phenomena, but we all figure that they begin "after" Pete Seeger, not with him.

As hard as he has tried to step back from the role of folk father, an insistent audience continues to push him to the front. As long as he's around, most folk fans reason, he'll be up front. It may be a burden for him, but it seems that some folks are just natural-born leaders.

Pete has been called "America's tuning fork," the man responsible for the folk movement and the folk revival. He's been at the very heart of it all since he went down to Asheville, North Carolina, while a student at Harvard. He traveled with Woody Guthrie, was an old pal of Burl Ives, Alan Lomax and Leadbelly. He sang with the Almanac Singers and then with the Weavers. He has toured the world in concert and as a good-will ambassador. He is passionately interested in social progress and in musical progress. That's the sort of guy he is.

He is also lank, lean, genuinely humble, shy, a real country boy at heart, articulate but not pedantic. And he thinks that children are very important, a feeling that wave upon wave of succeeding years of children's audiences reciprocate by saying: "Pete Seeger's important."

Pete has done more to focus interest on the five-string banjo, the guitar and a host of other folk instruments than almost anyone. He makes the playing of the instruments seem an accessible joy, and that is one of his greatest joys. And he makes everyone in an audience feel that he can throw his head back and sing. Some of his fans feel he works the audience-chorus too much and himself too little; this is not out of any sloth, but a keystone in his philosophy. The audience that sings together, Pete guesses, stays together.

So we have a certain push and pull here within the man whom most believe to be the key man in American folk music, the man who pulled the strings and

sang the song and set the tone for the whole last twenty-five years. From his "Darlin' Corey" album on Folkways to his slickest LP on Columbia, Pete's just been singing what's on his mind. He would deny, along with everything else, that he's much of a song-writer. After all, he only had a hand in "If I Had a Hammer" (with Lee Hays), "Where Have All the Flowers Gone?", "Turn, Turn, Turn" (with the writers of Ecclesiastes) and "The Big Muddy" (all on his own). He says he's had some luck with writing songs, but we'd rather call it some genius.

"Careless Love" is about as simple and direct a song as you might expect him to choose for the book. He's sung and recorded so many that it must have puzzled and perplexed him for a while to choose one. He'd probably say it was better than anything he ever wrote and go on to say that he can't sing it as well as "X" from the mountains or "Y" from the valleys. That's Pete.

Careless Love

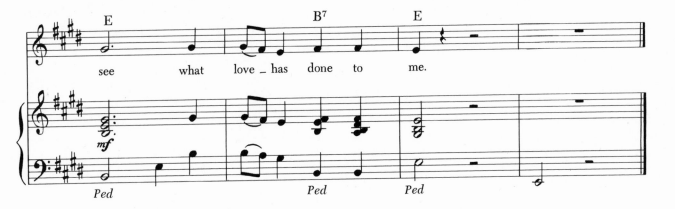

see what love — has done to me.

2 I love my mama and papa too.
I love my mama and papa too.
I love my mama and papa too.
I'd leave them both to go with you.

3 What, oh what, will mama say,
What, oh what, will mama say,
What, oh what, will mama say
When she learns I've gone astray?

4 Once I wore my apron low,
Once I wore my apron low,
Once I wore my apron low,
I couldn't scarcely keep you from my door.

5 Now my apron strings don't pin,
Now my apron strings don't pin,
Now my apron strings don't pin,
You pass my door and you don't come in.

6 Love, oh, love oh careless love.
Love, oh, love oh careless love.
Love, oh, love oh careless love.
You see what love has done to me.

FLATT & SCRUGGS

A FEW NAMES in folk song have become almost synonymous with their style. When one thinks of Bluegrass, one immediately thinks of Bill Monroe and of Lester Flatt and Earl Scruggs. There are many other able players of country string-band music, but these three have so helped develop and popularize the style that their names are hallmarks of their music.

Bluegrass is a music that stands firmly between folk tradition and commercial country music, between city and Nashville music. A direct line of descent can be drawn in Bluegrass, leading way back to Old World roots. The pipe and fiddle combinations that played Irish and Scottish jigs and hornpipes came to this country and were translated to fiddle, banjo and guitar. From the end of the nineteenth century until World War II there was a succession of lively little old-time string bands that played dance music and listening music. The work of some of these bands was revived by the New Lost City Ramblers, who helped focus attention on such historical groups as Gid Tanner and the Skillet-Lickers and the Carolina Tar Heels.

Bill Monroe and his brother Charlie had a similar sort of band in Kentucky, and in the years that followed World War II it was Monroe and His Bluegrass Boys that became the seed bed for nearly all the major Bluegrass bands that followed. As developed by Bill Monroe when Flatt and Scruggs were working with him, Bluegrass was a litttle folk orchestra, doing old-time or contemporary songs with an accomplished ensemble quality in which voices and instrumental lines wove in and out, often at brisk tempos, in a bright and colorful tapestry of sounds.

In time, Lester and Earl set off to form a band of their own, the Foggy Mountain Boys, which further solidified the appealing sound of Bluegrass. They were identified for years with Martha White Flour, even to the point of doing a singing commercial in Bluegrass style. They were even more popularly known by recording the theme song of "The Beverly Hillbillies" and the music for the movie *Bonnie and Clyde*.

Earl Scruggs is one of the great instrumental virtuosos of our time. In his deft hands the five-string banjo has become a new instrument, capable of rich and showy flights. Scruggs-picking, as it came to be known, is a supple three-finger style, developed out of an old roll when Scruggs was just a boy by the rural banjoists Snuffy Jenkins and Smith Hammett. In addition, the Scruggs peg, a small cam that enables the performer to change pitch on a string, added another element of flash to Scruggs's playing. Earl has just written a book, *Earl Scruggs and the Five-String Banjo,* which is being published almost simultaneously with this book.

While Earl Scruggs is the star, the entire Foggy Mountain Boys group works together with the polish and cohesiveness of a first-rate chamber ensemble. Lester Flatt's dulcet crooning, which reminds some of Bing Crosby, is a marked departure from the more athletic singing of Bill Monroe, another example of the diversity of Bluegrass. Then there are the wolfing sounds of the Dobro, a steel guitar fretted in the Hawaiian manner, the whump of the string bass and the overriding, chiding or brittle fiddle. It adds up to excitement that has been likened to the village orchestras of Eastern Europe or to rural Dixieland.

Flatt and Scruggs are among the strongest of traditionalists in the hotly commercial world of Nashville. They have, however, been able to accommodate themselves to both success and musical integrity. "Farther Along" is their favorite gospel song and one that they perform with great dignity and feeling.

Farther Along

Strong —in Slow 3

VERSE:

Tempt-ed and tried we're oft made to won - der Why it should be thus all the day long, ___ While there are oth - ers liv - ing a - bout us, Ne - ver mo - lest - ed though in the wrong. ___

REFRAIN—*More Smoothly:*

Far-ther a - long we'll know all a - bout it, Far-ther a - long we'll un-der-stand why; —— Cheer up, my broth - er, live in the sun - shine, We'll un - der - stand it all by and by. ——

2 Winter has come upon our loved ones,
Leaving our home so lonely and drear;
Then do we wonder why others prosper,
Living so wicked year after year.

3 "Faithful till death," said our loving Master,
A few more days to labor and wait;
Toils of the road will then seem as nothing,
As we sweep thru the beautiful gate.

4 When we see Jesus coming in glory,
When He comes from His home in the sky;
Then we shall meet Him in that bright mansion,
We'll understand it all by and by.

64

THE LINE from Paul Simon's song "Homeward Bound" about "a poet and a one-man band" could apply to many itinerant singers and their guitars. But the expression seems to be especially descriptive of Jesse Fuller, whose one-man band is unique in our folk-song roster.

Fuller is best known for his classic song "San Francisco Bay Blues" and for his unusual combination instrument, the fotdella. Perhaps he should enjoy even greater acclaim for his whole style of happy ragtime blues, which has had such influence on so many urban folk artists.

Jesse Fuller was born in Georgia in the last years of the nineteenth century. His childhood was the extreme hardship of a poor Negro orphan boy. He worked as a water boy for work gangs on river levees and soon found solace, and some money, with a guitar and harmonica.

He finally broke out of the Deep South around the end of World War II, settling in California. He continued to earn his living as a day laborer, working on construction jobs, with railway gangs, circuses, on film sets, wherever the jobs would take him. At one period he was operating a jackhammer by day and his fotdella by night.

This one-man band combination consists of his own guitar playing, a kazoo and a mouth harp rigged to his neck with metal braces that allow him to alternate freely between the two mouth instruments. The rhythmic base is established with the most unusual part of this contraption, a sawed-off, neckless string bass that is activated and plucked by use of a foot pedal! Against the raw and lively voice of Fuller, this instrumental stew sets up a charming interplay.

In this fashion Fuller was working in run-down clubs of Haight Street in San Francisco long before the hippies arrived. His song "San Francisco Bay Blues" was picked up by Rambling Jack Elliott and soon made the rounds of the folk and pop world.

The songs of Jesse Fuller fall into a category that is fascinating but hard to define. His blues songs tend to have a happy, dancing quality, a sort of "laughing at trouble" posture. His rhythmic approach is that of rural ragtime, clearly from another era but quite welcome to modern ears. His work is similar to the old jug-band approach, except for instrumentation. Some observers have even likened him to Leadbelly, but the over-all effect of the two performers is considerably different.

One must bear in mind that Jesse Fuller is an original.

For this collection Jesse Fuller has chosen "Raise a Ruckus."

JESSE FULLER

Raise a Ruckus

2 My old master said to me,
   Raise a ruckus tonight,
When he'd die he'd set me free,
   Raise a ruckus tonight. .
He lived so long his head got bald,
   Raise a ruckus tonight,
He got out o' the notion of dying at all,
   Raise a ruckus tonight.

3 Old hen sitting on a fodder stack,
   Raise a ruckus tonight,
Hawk came along and struck her in the back,
   Raise a ruckus tonight.
Old hen flew and the biddies too,
   Raise a ruckus tonight,
What in the world is the rooster gonna do?
   Raise a ruckus tonight.

UBIQUITOUS and *tireless* are two words that characterize Oscar Brand. The lean, youthful performer has successfully pursued half a dozen careers in music, returning, inevitably, to his earliest passion —folk song.

Although his career stretches well back into the first urban folk revival of the 1940s, Oscar has always kept pace with the times. In recent years he has been one of our leading jet-age folk singers, running TV shows out of Toronto and New York simultaneously and still, somehow, finding time to work on Broadway musicals, recordings, books and his long-time radio show on WNYC, New York.

If Oscar keeps himself mobile and active as a performer, this is simply a reflection of his approach toward repertory. On the more than fifty LP albums that he has recorded over the years, he has, perhaps run through, a greater range of material than any other singer. A singer who can turn from children's songs to humor songs to bawdy ditties without any appreciable loss of personal identity or stylistic grasp is indeed versatile.

Oscar Brand was born in Winnepeg in 1920, left Canada, finally settled in New York. During World War II he headed an Army psychology unit and, as his concerts will attest, he also learned a lot of servicemen's songs. At the end of the war he became folk-music coordinator on New York's municipal radio station, beginning the weekly "Folk Song Festival" shows that have played host over the years to folk singers both famous and obscure.

His chief non-folk-music activity has been in the production of films, from industrials to documentaries. Oscar has nearly fifty such films to his credit,

OSCAR

BRAND

for which he either wrote the script or score or did the narration. Other scripts include a series for the National Lutheran Council, and he has been the music director for the NBC-TV children's show "Exploring." His Canadian TV show is the weekly "Let's Sing Out!", which is shot on Canadian college campuses as was our American "Hootenanny" show.

Theater has also attracted Oscar. He and Paul Nassau did the words and music for *The Joyful Noise*, and in 1968 they wrote the score for the stage production of *The Education of H°y°m°a°n K°a°p°l°a°n.*

Still, Oscar keeps returning to folk music and has become one of the "Kilroy Was Here" types of the folk movement. Service on the Board of Directors of the Newport Folk Festival was just one of his public-service benefactions. To his legion of fans, the benefactions start every time Oscar grabs a guitar and sails into a performance. He is perhaps the most delightful performer for children's audiences anywhere. His humor and charm are a joy to watch.

In choosing for this collection "Bonavista Harbor" Oscar alludes to "the swinging lilt of the tune and the carefree tilt of the words. Besides," he adds with typical whimsicality, "I was born in Canada." With some more of his playfulness, he added: "If they make a feature-length movie out of these comments, I want free tickets to the premiere."

Bonavista Harbor

Gaily

VERSE:

Lots of fish in Bo - na - vist' Har - bor,
Lots of fish - ing down a - round here, Boys and girls go
fish - ing to - ge - ther, For - ty four miles from Car - bo - near.

Copyright © 1963 by Oscar Brand, Gypsy Hill Music.
All rights reserved. Used by permission.

2   Mother, she got up in the morning,
She got up in a heckuva tear,
Tore her nightie top to bottom,
Father says, "Now I don't care."

3   Sally goes to church on Sunday,
Not to pray and not to hear,
But to see the fellow from Fortune,
That was round here fishing last year.

4   Sally's goin' to have a baby,
Father says, "Now I don't care,
For I like the fellow from Fortune,
That was round here fishing last year."

COLLECTING was the greatest sport of the folk revival. For a while we collected songs, recordings, tapes, pictures. Then we began to collect native folk singers, befriended them, brought them to our city and college festivals and into our lives.

One of the first, and one of the truest, of the native folk singers was the gracious, gentle Kentucky singer Jean Ritchie. Jean sort of collected herself and came North to tell us on so many levels what life in the Southern mountains was really like. Because of her keen mind, her ability to communicate, in speech and music, and her total involvement in the native folk arts, Jean Ritchie became a special sort of person to us.

Ed McCurdy once remarked of Jean, "She left the hills but the hills never left her." Thus it was that, while being a performer, mother and urbanite, Jean Ritchie remained one of the constants of the revival. From that first Newport Folk Festival in 1959, or even before, until her wonderful expansive recording for Warner Brothers that included new songs, and in her book, *Singing Family of the Cumberlands,* Jean Ritchie reminded us of the "simple gifts" on which American rural life was structured.

The youngest of a family of fourteen children,

Jean was reared in the quaintly named town of Viper, Kentucky. Breaking with the rural isolation, Jean went on to the University of Kentucky, earned a Phi Beta Kappa key and went to New York to do social work. But the pull of folk singing was too great, and Jean became increasingly in demand to relive her childhood days of play-party songs and square dances and dulcimer tunes. How many thousands have gotten their first, formative contact with the American native folk tradition through Jean cannot be computed.

In 1952, with her husband, George Pickow, the photographer, Jean went on a Fulbright scholarship to the British Isles and Ireland to trace her family's three hundred songs back to their Old World roots. In performance and on recording, Jean connected her own past with her ancestral past. The storybook quality of her personal reminiscences did much to lay the groundwork in the 1950s for the rage of field trips of the 1960s. By her quiet presence, Jean seemed a walking beacon light for the great folk revival.

To choose a favorite song for this collection was a chore, since "I have more than 100 favorites." Here, she tells us, is "The Day Is Past and Gone," which "I learned in my very young days when I tagged along with Mom Ritchie to Sunday meeting at the Little Zion—Regular Baptist—Church in Jeff, Kentucky. It is one of the old 'lining out' hymns, and, although it is sad, there is great dignity and beauty in its sadness."

JEAN
RITCHIE

71

The Day Is Past and Gone

re - mem - ber ___ well, _____ The ___ hour _____

___ of ___ death _____ is ___ near. _____

2 We lay our garments by
Upon our beds to rest;
So Time will soon disrobe us all
Of what we now possess.

3 Lord, keep us safe this night,
Secure from all our fears.
May angels guard us while we sleep
Till morning light appears.

4 And when our days are past
And we from time remove,
O may we in Thy bosom rest,
The bosom of Thy love.

IMAGINE how difficult it might be to have to choose one person to symbolize all of American folk music. And yet if one were asked to do the same of Negro gospel song, the name that would undoubtedly be most often proposed would be Mahalia Jackson.

Although this rich field of modern religious music has thousands of great voices, groups and choirs, Mahalia is pre-eminent. She attained this position through her great musical gifts, her noble bearing and position and through the unassailable depth of her conviction.

Miss Jackson has taken songs of religious devotion from store-front churches to the leading auditoriums of the world. She has been seen at the Inaugural of President Kennedy, in prisons and hospitals, in revival-meeting tents, and in Philharmonic Hall in New York and its equivalents in Berlin and Tel Aviv.

Granddaughter of a slave, Mahalia was the third-born of six children. She was born in the musical cauldron of New Orleans in 1911 and grew up amid the sound of such great blues singers as Ma Rainey and Bessie Smith, to whom she has often been compared. The blues, however, lost a great voice when Mahalia decided that she would sing only religious songs rather than blues.

Although many modern gospel songs are heavily influenced by blues or jazz, Mahalia always tried to keep her music on the spiritual plane. "Blues are the songs of despair," she once wrote. "Gospel songs are the songs of hope. When you sing gospel, you have the feeling there is a cure for what's wrong, but when you are through with the blues, you've got nothing to rest on," she explained.

The size, sweep and majesty of Mahalia Jackson's voice electrified listeners and commentators alike. The great Negro writer Langston Hughes was proud to call himself "the first newspaper columnist in America to write about her." The novelist Ralph Ellison once described her music as "all joy and exultation and swing, but it is nonetheless religious music."

Although she never learned to read music, Miss Jackson is one of the great self-taught voices of our age. As a child, she turned to music "because I was lonely," and in later years her music was to assuage the loneliness, the despair and the sadness of others.

As the civil-rights movement grew during the 1960s, Mahalia Jackson turned her voice increasingly toward the songs of hope and freedom on which the movement was running. At the historic March on Washington in August 1963, Mahalia Jackson's voice sounded loud and clear from the steps of the monument built to honor Abraham Lincoln.

MAHALIA JACKSON

Balm in Gilead

Slow and Smooth

REFRAIN:

There _ is a balm in Gi - le - ad To make the wound - ed whole, _ There _ is a balm in Gi - le - ad To heal the sin - sick soul.

VERSES:

1. Some-times I feel dis - cour-aged, And think my work's in - vain, But

to Refrain

then the Ho - ly Spir - it Re - vives my soul a - gain. ___

2. If you can't pray like Pe - ter, If you can't pray like Paul, Go

to Refrain

home and tell your neigh - bor, "He died to save us all." ___

Earl's movie score from *A Walk in the Sun.*
His cantata "Giants in the Land."

His recently written Concerto for Banjo and Orchestra, which was performed by the Boston Pops under Arthur Fiedler, with Eric Weissberg as soloist.

This is quite an impressive roster of work for any composer. If you could familiarize yourself with it all, you might understand why I feel so strongly that Earl Robinson has been underrated and underappreciated by American music audiences.

EARL ROBINSON

GREAT composers have always taken their nourishment from the folk language of their cultures. Bach, Mozart, Brahms and Bartok are a few of the giants who took their inspiration from their native folk art.

Earl Robinson, one of America's greatest and least appreciated composers, has also built solidly on the folk music of his culture. His knowledge of American folk music has greatly enriched his work, and his knowledge of the life and problems of his country has, in turn, enriched his total art.

Earl's melodies are superb. He can create long, moving lines virtually unmatched by other American composers. It would be most worthwhile for young composers—or any listeners, for that matter —to hunt up some of Earl's too little-known works. It is not extravagant to call them "masterpieces." Consider, for example:

"When I Grow Up," a children's cantata.

The opera *Sandhog,* which he wrote with Waldo Salt.

"Rose of Sharon," a love song from an unproduced opera called *One Foot in America.*

His well-known works, of course: "Joe Hill," "The House I Live In," "Ballad for Americans," "The Lonesome Train."

Earl had written for Hollywood and endured the misery of its blacklist. But he is, like so many past victims of the blacklist, currently re-establishing himself there.

Earl has two recollections of how he came to folk song, the "official" and the "unofficial" paths. The first route was as a trained musician, a trained musician "with a social instinct." The unofficial way, which he never realized until much, much later, was around a family campfire on Puget Sound where they all harmonized Stephen Foster and the pop hits with ukulele and guitar. From this, he moved through the music school of the University of Washington, from which he graduated in 1933, to a day on the podium of the New York Philharmonic.

Earl's songs and singing are partially represented on an old Folkways disk, "A Walk in the Sun." His famous "Ballad for Americans," written with John LaTouche, was recorded by Paul Robeson on Victor in 1940 and later rereleased as an LP by Vanguard. The full recording and performance of the works of Earl Robinson is a project that is certainly long overdue.

In choosing "John Henry" for this collection, Earl was inevitably attracted to its melody but also to "the magnificence of the story and the strength and beauty of the poetry." He remembers "desperately trying to fire up a rather effete poetry society with the power of the 'John Henry' lines." While conceding the fact that "Freudian psychiatrists have a field day with the lyrics," which have been called "a gargantuan bawdy joke," one man who knows what it takes for even a trained musician to craft a great song, concludes "I prefer to remember John Henry as a great folk giant."

John Henry

Fast and Strong

When John Hen - ry was a lit - tle ba - by

Sit - tin' on his dad - dy's knee, Well he picked up a ham - mer and a

lit - tle piece of steel, "Ham - mer's gon - na be the death of

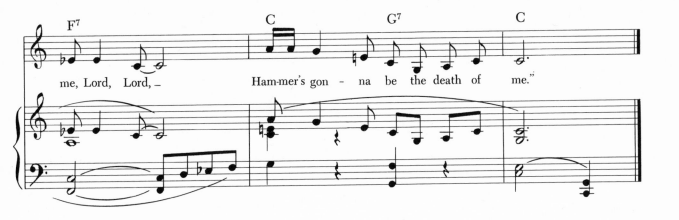

me, Lord, Lord, — Ham-mer's gon - na be the death of me."

2 The captain said to John Henry,
"I'm gonna bring that steam drill around,
I'm gonna bring that steam drill out on the job,
I'm gonna whup that steel on down,
       Lord, Lord!
Gonna whup that steel on down."

3 John Henry told his captain,
"Lord, a man ain't nothing but a man,
But before I'd let your steam drill beat me down,
I'd die with a hammer in my hand,
       Lord, Lord!
Die with a hammer in my hand!"

4 John Henry said to his shaker,
"Shaker, why don't you sing?
Because I'm swinging thirty pounds from my hips on down;
Just listen to that cold steel ring,
       Lord, Lord!
Listen to that cold steel ring."

5 Now the captain said to John Henry,
"I believe that mountain's caving in."
John Henry said right back to the captain,
"Ain't nothing but my hammer sucking wind.
       Lord, Lord!
Ain't nothing but my hammer sucking wind."

6 Now the man that invented the steam drill,
He thought he was mighty fine;
But John Henry drove fifteen feet,
The steam drill only made nine.
       Lord, Lord!
The steam drill only made nine.

7 John Henry hammered in the mountains,
His hammer was striking fire,
But he worked so hard, it broke his poor heart
And he laid down his hammer and he died.
       Lord, Lord!
He laid down his hammer and he died.

ROBERT De CORMIER

De CORMIER is a many-talented musician; a fine conductor, composer, arranger and singer. He has had his greatest success as an arranger, with numerous albums to his credit.

The role of the arranger has always been in great dispute during the whole of the folk revival. How far can one go before arranging becomes tampering, before resetting becomes distorting. This is a seemingly endless argument, with equally vocal protagonists on both sides.

De Cormier is not the only man to bring a substantial classical training to the problem of developing appropriate arrangements of folk music. But he was one of the very first so trained who did have a genuine love and wide knowledge of folk music. This understanding of the idiom, together with his Juilliard background, has made Bob welcome in both camps. It was under Bob De Cormier's tutelage and sponsorship I went to work for Harry Belafonte. Together we researched material and wrote arrangements. I did my first arrangements for Harry under what I like to call Bob's "protection." (He would rehearse the orchestra or singing group in the new arrangement without mentioning to Harry or the other artists that it was mine. But if Harry expressed favor about the arrangement, Bob would say: "Milt did it." It's a form of generosity I haven't found since then in the commercial world.)

Bob has a beautiful lyric baritone voice, and with his wife Louise, has recorded folk albums that are gems.

The traditional song Bob chose for our collection is one associated with Robert Burns. This is not surprising, since De Cormier has been greatly interested in Burns. Some years ago he performed settings of the Scottish poet's work in a Town Hall program.

"Green Grow the Rashes, O!" is an unashamed toast to woman. The tune Bobby Burns used was found in *Walsh's Country Dances*, a mid-eighteenth-century collection. The Burns lyrics pop up as well in the famous "Merry Muses of Caledonia," the master folk anthology that Burns collected, edited and, as is often the style of folk poets, rewrote.

Green Grow the Rashes, O!

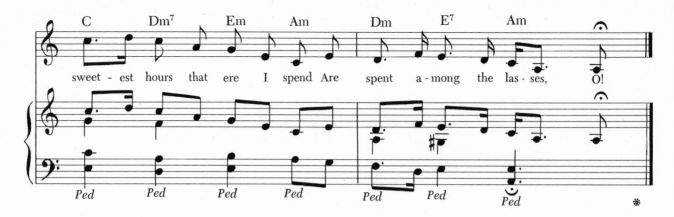

sweet - est hours that ere I spend Are spent a - mong the las - ses, O!

2   The wardly race may riches chase,
An' riches still may fly them, O!
An' though at last they catch them fast.
Their hearts can ne'er enjoy them, O!

3   Gie mie a cannie hour at e'en,
My arms about my dearie, O!
And wardly cares and wardly men
May a' gae tapsalteerie, O!

4   An' you sae douce, wha sneer at this,
Ye're nought but senseless asses, O!
The wisest man in the warld e'er saw,
He dearly lo'ed the lasses, O!

5   Auld Nature swears the lovely dears
Her noblest works she classes, O!
Her 'prentice han' she tried on man,
An' then she made the lasses, O!

(v. 3) cannie—quiet; tapsalteerie—topsy-turvy;
(v. 4) sae—so; douce—sedate, sober.

JACK ELLIOTT

"HE SOUNDS more like me than I do," Woody Guthrie was alleged to have said of Rambling Jack Elliott. For a good ten years before the arrival of Bob Dylan and of Woody's son Arlo, Jack was the chief proponent of the famous Guthrie hard-traveling tradition.

Jack is the son of a Brooklyn physician. It was a source of wonder that he assimilated the speech, the music, the wit and the manner of Guthrie, his mentor and traveling companion. But, as the years passed and Jack Elliott grew and prospered, his material, his stage manner and his performing personality became less Guthrie and more Elliott. Still, the dominating early influence, the Oklahoma hills and valleys, stayed with Jack.

The footloose rambler is one of the undying figures of romance in American life. He symbolizes the Orphic rambler, the spaciousness of our frontier, the freedom of movement in America, the man who is a citizen of everywhere. This was the type of troubadour-minstrel that Guthrie was, that Elliott became and that hundreds of young music-makers would later emulate.

Jack Elliott represented a real link between the era of the first folk revival of World War II and the current revival. From his earliest years Jack was fascinated with cowboys in general and Gene Autry in particular. "Then," he once reminisced, "I met a real cowboy and found out he didn't look like Gene Autry at all. I've hated Autry ever since and campaigned against him for years."

Rambling Jack rambled away from school periodically, to join rodeos and to get away from dull middle-class life. Then Jack found a reason to ramble when he fell under the sway of Woody Guthrie. As recounted in *Newsweek* in 1961, "Elliott was a 20-year-old with big dreams and little hope. But, from the moment they met a few months later, Elliott began to live the life of his older friend, singing only his songs, talking in his clipped, hoarse drawl, and accepting Guthrie's tales of life on the road as his own...."

Woody went into the hospital in 1954 and Jack headed for the new frontiers of Europe. There, for a time, he was the leading white American folk singer, with an enormous grip on his audience. Upon his return to America in the late 1950s he found a country in the grip of its folk boom, looking for people like Jack Elliott. To one such youngster, Bob Dylan, Elliott was to pass along the enthusiasm for the Guthrie mystique, as well as a good hunk of the Elliott mystique.

Jack sings scat songs now and works sometimes with jazz instrumentation and will try anything. He plays one of the wickedest guitars in or out of show business. He tells a shaggy cow story better than nearly anyone on the urban folk scene. He always seems to have arrived half an hour late in a pickup truck that broke down on the highway. Maybe it's all because his stated slogan is: "You don't learn much traveling first class."

A Picture from Life's Other Side

Moderately

VERSE:

In this world's migh-'ty gall-'ry of pic-tures _____ Hang scenes that are paint-ed from life; _____ A pic-ture of love and of pas-sion, _____ A pic-ture of love and of strife. _____

picture of youth and of beau - ty, _____ Old age and the blush -ing young

bride, _____ All hang on the wall but the

sad - est of all Is the pic - ture from life's oth - er side. _____

REFRAIN:

'Tis a pic - ture from life's oth - er side, _____

85

Some-one who fell by the way; _____ A life has gone out with the tide _____ That may have been hap - py one day; _____ Some poor old mo - ther at home, _____ Watch - ing and wait - ing a - lone, _____ A - long - ing to hear from her

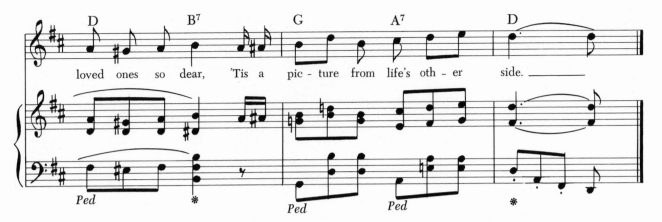

loved ones so dear, 'Tis a pic - ture from life's oth – er side. _____

2   The first scene is that of a gambler
Who spends all his money at play,
Draws his dead mother's ring from his finger
That she wore on her wedding day—
His last earthly treasure, he stakes it,
Bows his head that his shame he might hide.
When they lifted his head, they found he was dead—
'Tis a picture from life's other side.

3   The next scene is that of two brothers
Whose paths in life different ways led—
The one was in luxury living,
The other one begged for his bread.
One dark night they met on a highway;
"Your money or life," the thief cried.
Then he took with his knife his dear brother's life—
'Tis a picture from life's other side.

WILL
HOLT

ALTHOUGH Will Holt loves traditional folk song and has done a highly creditable job of performing it, his reputation was made through the songs of the modern German composer Kurt Weill.

After years of singing in concerts and cabarets, Will teamed up with Martha Schlamme for a program called "The World of Kurt Weill in Song" at the off-Broadway Jan Hus House, the Howff and One Sheridan Square. Reviewers were unanimous in praising the spirit and theatrical sweep that Holt brought to the songs of Weill and Bertolt Brecht. Jerry Tallmer in the *New York Post* wrote: "there comes this Down East Yankee (Mr. Holt) out-Berlining the Berliners with a tough, fine program. . . . He has more of Brecht-Weill in him than most *Threepenny Operas* you'll ever see. . . ."

The Down East Yankee attended Exeter Academy and Williams College before moving to Aspen, Colorado, to study privately with Richard Dyer-Bennett. After travel in Europe and a Korean War stint in the Air Force, he began performing professionally.

Will was a mainstay of the Crystal Palace in St. Louis. His sophisticated manner and musicianship brought him next to Manhattan's Village Vanguard and Blue Angel, to Chicago's Gate of Horn and San Francisco's hungry i.

The singer and guitarist also took a turn at songwriting, producing such as "Raspberries, Strawberries," "Lemon Tree" and "Till the Birds Sing in the Morning." All of them demonstrated his lyricism and his grasp of that element of contemporary songwriting, the durability of a folk-style tradition.

Somehow all that had gone before was only a prologue to the work Will did in "The World of Kurt Weill." Being essentially a theater piece, it required a stage sense, which he had, an ability to invest the characters of each song with life. His version of "Mack the Knife," for all the many interpretations it has had, is considered a classic. And Will Holt's rendition of Weill's "September Song" could stand against any. The show was written and directed by Mr. Holt, one of the staunchest admirers of Kurt Weill as a major composer of our time. In broadening out to such music in the early 1960s, Will Holt was presaging a later development among folk performers who loved tradition and yet wanted to reflect their own time.

When it comes to traditional song, Will is still at home. For this collection he has chosen "She Moved Through the Fair." He says of this lovely song from Ireland:

"This song has always fascinated me for two reasons: the enigma of the lovers. Is she on earth or is she dead? Is he dreaming? Will there be a wedding? It's a marvelous drama in three stanzas, and so beautifully worded by Padraic Colum, who translated the text from the Gaelic. And secondly, the rhythm and the melody of this song. The melody is so haunting and so right for this text, and the rhythm keeps holding for a moment and then releasing, like a tension and a relaxation. All in all, I don't know any song which has given me, as a performer, more constant pleasure."

She Moved Through the Fair

Slowly and Freely

VERSE:

D

My — true love said to me,

C   D   C

— "My— mo-ther won't mind, And my fa-ther _____ won't

D   Em   F MAJ⁷   D

slight you for your lack of kind," ___ And she stepp'd _____ a-way

Lyrics by Padric Colum
from "Irish Country Songs" by Herbert Hughes
Copyright 1909 by Boosey & Co. Renewed 1936.
Copyright and renewal assigned to Boosey & Hawkes, Inc.
Reprinted by permission.

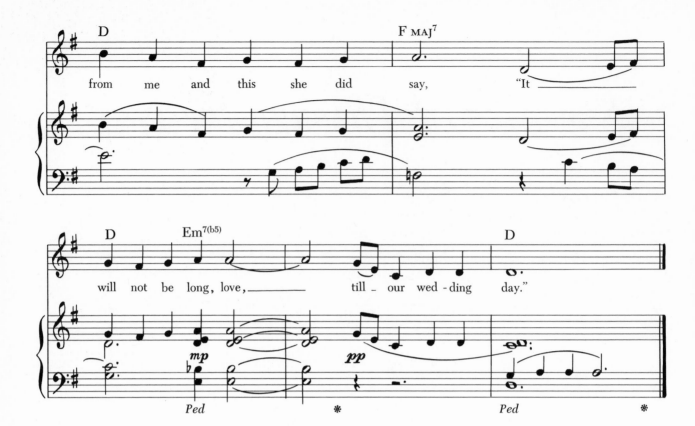

2   As she stepped away from me and she moved through the fair,
And fondly I watched her move here and move there,
And then she turned homeward with one star awake,
Like the swan in the evening moves over the lake.

3   Last night she came to me, my dead love came in,
So softly she came that her feet made no din;
As she laid her hand on me and this she did say,
"It will not be long, love, till our wedding day."

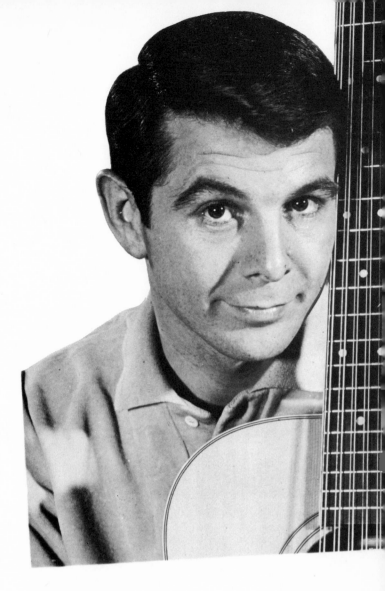

SOME OF the most influential members of any music community are fully appreciated only by other musicians. This is true of Bob Gibson.

Dozens of the younger city folk musicians studied the work of Gibson, incorporated it into their own style and often became better known than their model. Vocally and instrumentally, Bob Gibson achieved a fluency that helped set a style for many performers.

Gibson has great vitality. Each time he sings a song it seems fresh and new, partly because of the songs he chooses, partly because of his own intensity.

But his career has not been easy. He was often exhausted, his voice would disappear, he could not conceal his great sensitivity and uncertainty. And so Gibson's erratic performances became almost legendary. Yet his real admirers remained; they knew his great moments were worth waiting for.

Bob was born in New York in 1931, the son of a chemical engineer who had been a professional singer early in life. The son's first recognition came to him in Cleveland, spread to Chicago and then around the country. It was Bob who, while working at the Gate of Horn in Chicago, discovered the eighteen-year-old Joan Baez and presented her at the first Newport Folk Festival in 1959. Ironically, Joan's star rose while Gibson's flickered.

Although much in Bob Gibson's playing and singing is modern and sophisticated, one can hear an enormous understanding of American folk tradition. This understanding, however, does not make him an imitator but an interpreter of an older music for a younger audience. Always with vitality, he would spin out ribbons of banjo, 12-string or 6-string guitar music, and his velvety, at best, vocal texture would seem to glide over a song rather than to dwell on it.

There is so much that is contemporary about the work of Bob Gibson that it seems strange to recall that he recorded in the middle 1950s, long before the Kingston Trio was organized, that he had done dozens of tunes on the old Stinson and Riverside labels that would give later folk students a library.

BOB GIBSON

Hard Is the Fortune (WAGONER LAD)

Moderately

Hard is the for - tune of — all wo - man - kind, She's al - ways con - trolled, — she's al - ways con - fined. Con - trolled by her pa - rents un - til she's a wife, Then a

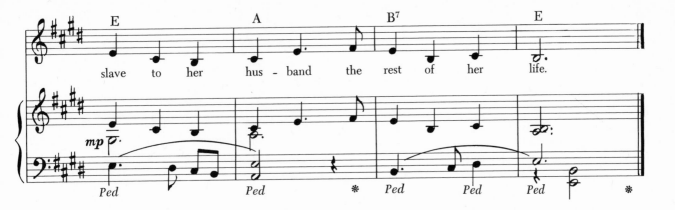

slave to her hus - band the rest of her life.

2 My horses are hungry,
They won't eat your hay;
So goodbye, little darlin'
I'm going away.

3 Your parents don't like me,
They say I'm too poor;
They say I'm not worthy
To enter your door.

O F ALL the travelers across the bridge from Nashville to Newport, few seem more at home in both places than Johnny Cash. He has brought the liveliness of country and western music to the folk scene and the sense of the contemporary, involved balladeer to the country scene.

Johnny's career has roughly paralleled that of Elvis Presley's, storming out of the Memphis rockabilly field into national prominence ten years ago.

JOHNNY CASH

However, there are likenesses in him to a "grand tradition of country music." In *The Country Music Story*, Robert Shelton wrote:

"... In other aspects, the personality of Cash reminds one of Rodgers and Williams. All were gifted, driven men with almost embattled lives of hardship, either from the outer world or from the private torments that they inflicted upon themselves ... beyond his 'modern sound,' Cash sings with a deep soulfulness that is convincing of his sincere identification with his lyrics. He is proud of his origins as a cotton farmer from Arkansas. He is proud of his descent as a Cherokee Indian. ..."

Johnny Cash was born in 1932 to a family that lived a life of hard poverty near Kingsland, Arkansas. No surprise that John has chosen for this book a famous railroading song, because he was born and reared within the whistle-blow of the St. Louis and Southwestern Railroad. "A passing train," John used to recall, "might mean that Daddy was coming home."

Radio was young John's link to the pop mainstream, while his own life and sharecropping environment was all the link needed to folk tradition. Even as late as 1946 the Cashes used kerosene lamps

for light and wood stoves for the cooking and heating. While serving in the Army, John overcame a long-standing fear of performing and began to sing for his buddies. His first recording was released in June 1955. But it took still another year for him to break out, and by 1956 his recording of his own song "I Walk the Line" dominated the country hit charts.

The years since then have been a mixture of triumph and problems. Enormously well-selling singles and LPs on the Columbia label have logged the upswing, while throat trouble and desultory performances have marked the downswing. When Johnny Cash went to Newport and his large and baleful voice soared across the heads of the audience, he was in a special heaven all his own. As a musician's greatest gesture of friendship to a colleague, he gave his guitar to Bob Dylan at Newport in 1963. In early 1968 Johnny married June Carter of the great musical "Carter Family."

The number of railroad songs that Cash has recorded would run from here to the headquarters of the Union Pacific. None could more embody the singer's strength, ruggedness or country background than "Rock Island Line."

94

Rock Island Line

New words and new music adaptation by Huddie Ledbetter.
Edited with new additional material by Alan Lomax.
Copyright © 1959 Folkways Music Publishers, Inc., New York, N.Y.
Used by permission.

2 I may be right and I may be wrong,
Know you're gonna miss me when I'm gone.

3 A, B, C, Double X, Y, Z,
Cats in the cupboard but they don't see me.

96

I WORKED with Harry Belafonte for approximately six years, first as his pianist, then a singer in an accompanying chorus. Next I worked as an assistant conductor, then arranger, and finally conductor. If there were any jobs around the Belafonte organization I didn't work at, it is only because I hadn't heard about them.

I learned so much from this experience, from this man, that it is not easy to fully document details. Perhaps the most important lesson Harry taught was on the art of hard work. Harry would roll up his sleeves and go to work on a song for eight or ten or even twelve hours. He was almost like a construction worker, building a song by experimentation to an intense experience. What concentration, and what feeling!

This learning and growing continued for me through the period in 1960 when I made a round-the-world trip with him and discovered new singers and new songs, especially of the Pacific areas. All of this added up to a fascinating six years spent with what I might call Belafonte University. As with any good schooling, the effects linger on.

Although Harry was clearly one of the great contributors to the folk-song revival that began in the 1950s, it became very fashionable to put him down. The ethnic determinists were harsh on him for musical liberties and his "popularization." Some reviewers were harsh on him for having become such an "organization man," never putting on any number without a cast of thousands. Most of this criticism was blatantly unfair, but Harry braced his shoulders and took it like a trouper.

If there were critics there were also a lot of denizens of the show-business jungle who respected Harry Belafonte for his musical contributions, his charm, his generosity, his artistic and social commitment. At one point Harry's fostering of young talent was among the most wholesome things ever encountered in show business. He had offered tuition, coaching, living expenses and production assistance for young talents. Among those to benefit from this were Miriam Makeba, Hugh Masekela, an African trumpet player, and Valentine Pringle, a bass-baritone.

Belafonte was born in New York but moved to Jamaica, in the Caribbean, for five years while a boy. He attended high school in New York and joined the Navy for two years in 1944. He became a member of the American Negro Theater, joined the Dramatic Workshop, where he studied with Marlon Brando and Tony Curtis and where he helped discover himself as a singer. After a turn as a pop crooner Harry ran a restaurant in Greenwich Village and there fell into the folk scene. Late in 1950 Belafonte teamed up with the guitarist Millard Thomas to help build a repertoire of folk songs. He got a gig at the Village Vanguard and was off and running on a new career.

From there on in it was an upward spiral of success and broadening activity. Recording for RCA Victor, making films, doing his show around the world, getting deep into television production, Belafonte was soon a star of great proportions. The Kingston Trio borrowed from his Calypso revival of the late 1950s to start the folk revival officially.

Harry Belafonte came back to America not as a star but as a deeply committed person involved in the Negro rights movement. We saw him at the side of Martin Luther King, Jr.'s, widow, and we knew the degree of his involvement.

HARRY  BELAFONTE

I've Been 'Buked
and I've Been Scorned

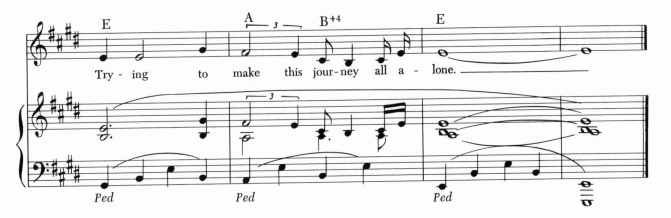

Try - ing to make this jour-ney all a - lone. _____

2 You may talk about me sure as you please.
You may talk about me sure as you please.
You may talk about me sure as you please.
Your talk'll never drive me down to my knees.

3 Jesus died to set me free.
Jesus died to set me free.
Jesus died to set me free,
Nailed to that cross on Calvary.

4 I've been 'buked and I've been scorned.
I've been 'buked and I've been scorned.
I've been 'buked and I've been scorned,
Trying to make this journey all alone.

IT WAS a full three or four years after her emergence as a star that Odetta stopped "shocking" her listeners. The first few encounters with her massive and powerful voice were always an unsettling surprise to most of us. After a time, we knew what to expect when she uncorked that sleeping giant in her throat, and we settled in for her fine, deep interpretations.

Odetta has been a central figure in the folk revival of the last ten years. She was always listed early among the important new figures in the revival, always counted among the top handful who represented an era. We followed her work on Tradition, Vanguard, Victor and Verve/Folkways as we followed her concerts and her steady career.

Odetta represents more than a voice. Because of her powerful size and gentle manner she seemed an embodiment to many of us of the Negro people, strong and noble and dignified. "Detta," as a few intimates call her, bears herself with the splendid quiescence of a queen who is able to meet the people at close hand and yet still retain a certain aristocratic detachment.

Musically, her story is one of challenge and response. Nothing, it seems, is outside her vocal or emotional range, from a little song like "One Grain of Sand" to a great cantata, "Ballad for Americans." She sings of freedom and she sings of joy, she sings of politics and of whimsy, of the old and the young, of the lost and the loved. She has a maternal manner and bearing.

A music teacher had wanted Odetta Felious to pursue a career in classical music. But Odetta felt that classical music was too abstract for her, too "detached," as one observer described it, "from a familiar human situation." Here is how Odetta has explained the meaning of folk music to her:

"There are songs where I speak for others, and there are those which are very subjective, where I speak for myself. When singing, I can often conjure up images to myself. . . . It's almost as if I become a kind of spokesman for the persons of the song. I could be singing a song and find myself looking at a prison scene. . . . I'm almost standing outside of myself, seeing me on a work gang, and in my imagination I get the feeling of exhaustion, injustice, of all that is going on."

This special magic is one that all folk singers strive to attain but not all achieve. Because she has achieved it so often and with so many different sorts of material, we, the fortunate listeners, feel that the songs of Odetta are parts of a human drama. With that powerful, dark alto voice of hers (one she has stretched upward until she is a near soprano on top) and her human empathy, Odetta puts folk and music together as few others do. No longer a simple matter,

ODETTA

the music becomes complex, yet retains the emotional wallop of a hammer blow. This is how she sings "The Fox," "Another Man Done Gone," "He Had a Long Chain On," the famous "Freedom Trilogy" and hundreds of other works.

The years pass, Odetta deepens and expands her ability to communicate passionately in song. In the winter of 1968, at the memorial tribute to Woody Guthrie, her singing was perhaps at its greatest. Her performance was epochal. This "human music" quality she brings to "The Gallows Pole," the song she has chosen to express her involvement with both traditional folk song and traditional human justice.

The Gallows Pole

2 Papa, did you bring me silver?
Papa, did you bring me gold?
Did you come to see me hangin'
By the gallows pole?

3 Well, I couldn't bring no silver,
I didn't bring no gold.
Yes, I come to see you hangin'
By the gallows pole.

4   Hangman, hangman, slack your rope,
Slack it for a while,
Think I see my mother comin',
Ridin' many a mile.

5   Mama, did you bring me silver?
Mama, did you bring me gold?
Did you come to see me hangin'
By the gallows pole?

6   Well, I couldn't bring no silver,
I didn't bring no gold.
Yes, I come to see you hangin'
By the gallows pole.

7   Hangman, hangman, slack your rope,
Slack it for a while,
Think I see my sweetheart comin',
Ridin' many a mile.

8   Honey, did you bring me silver?
Honey, did you bring me gold?
Did you come to see me hangin'
By the gallows pole?

9   I brought you silver,
Brought you a little gold,
Didn't come to see you hangin'
By the gallows pole.

THEODORE BIKEL

"MR. EVERYWHERE" might be a suitable sobriquet for Theo Bikel. Beyond the sheer getting-around propulsion of the man, he manages, somehow, to keep his hand in a dozen stews, as long as the cause is humanitarian, musical or artistic.

Theo is one of the organizers, with Pete Seeger and George Wein, of the revamped Newport Folk Foundation and Festival. He is an activist with Actors' Equity, seeking, at every appropriate occasion, to broaden the scope of Federal aid to the arts. He is obdurately involved with civil rights, whether they pertain to Southern Negroes or World Jewry or minorities with less dramatic or more obscure problems.

On this level Theodore Bikel is a true "folknik," finding that his human concerns and his musical passions are all wrapped together. One would think that, for such an accomplished actor, music would have to be relegated to a very small role. But it isn't, Theo somehow always manages to get himself ensconced, with a guitar and a few score of willing ears, to play and sing and tell stories.

Bikel speaks and sings in more languages than most of us could readily identify. He is especially adept in the language and folklore of Eastern Europe and Israel, reflecting his own itinerant youth from Vienna to the Middle East. If there is a better interpreter of Russian Gypsy music about than Theo, let him step forward with his balalaika. If there is a performer more steeped in the songs of the Eastern European Jewish ghettos, let him speak. And if there is a more articulate and forthright singer of the bold new folk music of Israel than Theo, may my left hand wither, or some less frightening Biblical injunction.

Theo is a familiar face to world moviegoers, and his many characterizations include the Soviet U-boat captain in *The Russians Are Coming*, the Dutch officer in the film about the escaping prisoners and the Scottish cemetery caretaker in another film. The titles and credits are less to the point here than the breadth of nationalities and roles that Theo's work contains. So, too, in his equally full stage career, have there been roles as an Austrian uncle in *The Sound of Music* and as Tevye, the Sholem Aleichem character in *Fiddler on the Roof*.

This is why we can, with impunity, call Theodore Bikel "Mr. Everywhere." If the cause is artistic or humanitarian, he will be around. He likes to sing and tell stories and is a good man. It's good to have him on the folk scene.

Peat Bog Soldiers

Words by Wolfgang Langhoff and Esser;
last verse by Theodore Bikel.
Music by Rudi Goguel.
Copyright © 1965 by Stormking Music Inc.
All rights reserved. Used by permission.

104

2 Up and down the guards are pacing,
No one, no one can go through.
Flight would mean a sure death facing;
Guns and barbed wire greet our view.

3 But we show no grief, no sorrow,
Winter will in time be past,
Dawn will break on a joyful morrow,
Free men we shall be at last.

REFRAIN (3):

Then will the peat bog soldiers
March no more with their spades to the bog.
Then will the peat bog soldiers
March no more with their spades to the bog.

Left to right:
John Stewart,
Nick Reynolds,
Bob Shane

THE KINGSTON TRIO

THREE WHO MADE A REVOLUTION, that book about some bearded political revolutionists who changed world history, might, with a bit of tailoring and shaving, describe the Kingston Trio. Now, we'll grant you that our three cherubic, well-scrubbed and highly collegiate-looking fellows never regarded themselves as any sort of revolutionaries, never in the least considered themselves as anyone anxious to change the face of anything.

No, Nick Reynolds, Bob Shane and Dave Guard simply thought they would have a bit of fun singing, and before they knew it they had ushered in an era, a musical revolution, a total new life style. We know, of course, that folk music is the oldest music known to man, and we know that the Kingston Trio did not spring from a vacuum. There were antecedents of all sorts; there were pioneers and there were stars of American folk song long before the Kingston Trio ever hit its first conga drum.

But the turning point was clearly the break-out of the Kingstons. Once described as "rockless, roll-less and rich," the trio chose its name because it sounded both Ivy Leaguish and Calypsonian. The Ivy image prevailed, from crew cuts to button-down, short-sleeved shirts, though all three hailed from California. Dave attended Stanford while the other two went to Menlo College of Business Administration. Guard was said to have had something of a pre-beatnik look about him in student days.

Their appearance at the Purple Onion in San Francisco began to give a hint of things to come. It was apparent that they would turn truly professional, take voice lessons, acquire the managerial assistance of Frank Werber, and so on. Then came their first recording triumph, with "Tom Dooley," and both the trio and the revival were hitting in earnest in late 1958 and early 1959.

"Tom Dooley" was a traditional Southern mountain song that Frank Warner had collected from the singing of the late Frank Proffitt. The murder ballad had cropped up in a Lomax collection and nearly all the bases of the folk process had been touched. The "home run," however, was that a song of such background and history could possibly become a national hit. Clearly, the audience that had enjoyed such a song by such a group was quite a changed audience from the one that had just helped elevate Elvis Presley and a host of hard-rockers to stardom.

At the first Newport Folk Festival of 1959, it was clearly the Kingston Trio that was the leading box-office attraction. At first it was a strange meeting, the popular Kingstons on one hand, the Jean Ritchies on the other, and the Bob Gibsons standing uncomfortably in the middle. But, as with all new things, it just took a while to find a meeting ground and a mutuality of interest. The folk traditionalists and the more ethnically oriented members of the audience felt that some of the humor and styling of the Kingston Trio was a bit hard to take. But the more civilized of the old guard tolerated, and learned, ten years later, to understand that there is room for more than one approach to any music.

The Kingston Trio changed personnel some years ago when Dave Guard left for Australia and was replaced by John Stewart. And since then they switched to the Decca label from Capitol and have finally disbanded. They left their mark on the face of the revival. Their true worth and contribution will still be a source of debate, but the number of people they brought to folk music of a deeper kind must number in the hundreds of thousands.

Midnight Special

shoul - der, _____ Piece of pa - per in her hand, _____

She says to the Cap - tain: _____ "I want my man!"

REFRAIN:

Let the Mid - night Spe - cial _____ shine her light _ on

me, _____ Let the Mid - night Spe - cial _____

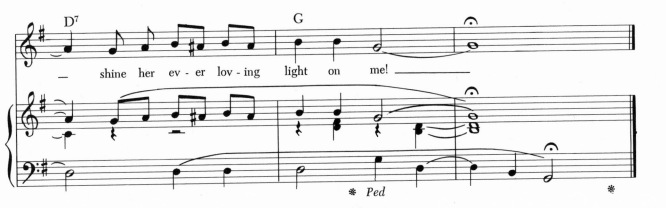

shine her ev - er lov - ing light on me!

2 If you ever go to Houston,
You better walk right;
You better not gamble
And you better not fight.
Mr. Bentley will arrest you,
He'll surely take you down;
Judge Nelson'll sentence you,
Then you're jailhouse bound.

3 Every Monday morning
When the ding-dong rings,
You go to the table,
See the same damn things;
And on the table,
There's a knife and pan,
Say anything about it,
You're in trouble with the man.

Greensleeves

REFRAIN:

Green-sleeves was all my joy, Green-sleeves was my delight. Green-sleeves was my heart of gold, And who but my Lady Green-sleeves.

2 I have been ready at your hand
To grant whatever you would crave,
I have both waged life and land,
Your love and good will for to have.

3 I bought thee petticoats of the best,
The cloth so fine as it might be,
I gave thee jewels for the chest,
And all this cost I spent on thee.

4 Well, I will pray to God on high,
That thou my constancy may'st see,
For I am still thy lover true;
Come once again and love me.

Buffalo Gals, Won't You Come Out Tonight?

Sprightly and Fast

VERSE: As I was walk-ing down the street,— Down the street,— down the street,— A love-ly gal I chanced to meet,— Oh! she was fair to see.

REFRAIN: Oh, Buf-fa-lo Gals — won't you come out to-night,

2 I asked her would she have some talk,
Have some talk, have some talk.
Her feet covered up the whole sidewalk,
As she stood close by me.

3 I asked her would she have a dance,
Have a dance, have a dance.
I thought that I might get a chance
To shake a foot with her.

THE CASUALTY rate among professional folk singers is high. With a mercurial audience that can change its interests and its stars with incredible ease, the durable professional singer must indeed be able to grow. This ability, which is a distinguishing characteristic, has helped keep the West Coast folk quartet, the Brothers Four, on the scene for many years.

The Brothers Four, college fraternity brothers, had no problem starting with a youthful image, tailor-made for the collegiate audience. That was how they came up, and that is the format they have built upon since 1959. They have a naturalness, an agreeable group personality, an unforced way with a song that rings true to the audiences.

From their earliest times together, Michael Kirkland, Dick Foley, Bob Flick and John Paine were singing together at the University of Washington "just for fun and free beer." An audition tape was sent to Columbia Records, and the singing then became a project "for fun and money." Because of their attractive and clean-cut appearance, the four boys were the perfect picture of one type of American college student.

But, on closer examination, one discovered that Mike, Dick, Bob and John were not just rah-rah boys —they read a lot, they talked about public issues, they repeated a familiar word, "growth," whenever they tried to appraise themselves as people and as performers.

This "growth" has taken them through more than a dozen LPs on the Columbia label, through a vast and ever-growing repertoire of folk, pop and show tunes, from Japan to Moscow to Stockholm to "Snake's Navel, New Mexico," their own name for the most provincial outpost they have ever visited.

Their work schedule would frighten the weak-of-heart. Usually a season involves more than 200 college concerts, dozens of TV appearances and, always, recording rehearsals and sessions. Fortunately, they enjoy as much harmony together off-stage as they do on.

They have often enjoyed more popularity abroad, especially in Japan, than at home in the U.S. Hard-working professionalism of their sort is not what the American public always associates with a folk group. Nor is college-age sensitivity and awareness usually associated with the clean-cut, all-American type. But the brothers Kirkland, Foley, Flick and Paine have all these elements mixed in believable proportions.

THE BROTHERS FOUR

Left to right: Bob Flick, Dick Foley, John Paine, Mike Kirkland

Follow the Drinking Gourd

Words and music by Paul Campbell
Copyright © 1951 Folkways Music Publishers, Inc., New York, N.Y.
Used by permission.

2 The river ends between two hills,
Follow the drinking gourd!
There's another river on the other side,
If you follow the drinking gourd.

3 The river bank makes a very good road;
The dead trees show you the way;
Left foot, peg-foot, traveling on,
Follow the drinking gourd.

4 Where the great big river meets the little river,
Follow the drinking gourd!
For the sailor boy's awaiting for to carry you to freedom,
If you follow the drinking gourd.

116

Shenandoah

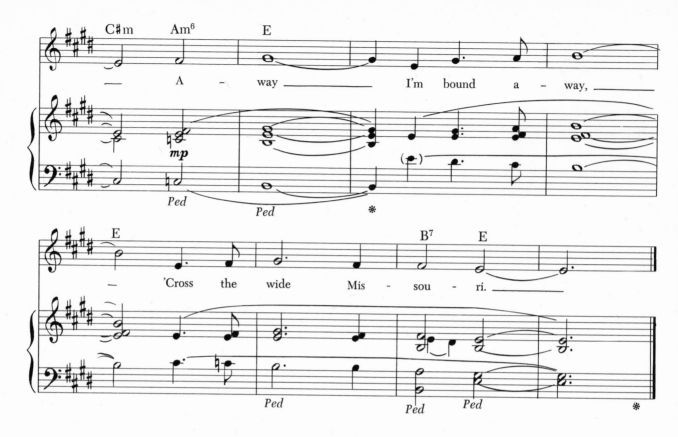

2 Oh Shenandoah, I love your daughter,
Away, you rolling river,
For her I'd cross the rolling water,
Away, I'm bound away, 'cross the wide Missouri.

3 Oh Shenandoah, I'm bound to leave you,
Away, you rolling river,
Oh Shenandoah, I'll not deceive you,
Away, I'm bound away, 'cross the wide Missouri.

Drill, Ye Tarriers, Drill

Fast and Strong
VERSE:

Ev - 'ry morn - in' at sev - en o' - clock ___ There's

twen - ty tar - ri - ers a - work - ing at the rock, And the boss comes a - long ___ and he

says, "Keep still, And come down heav - y on the cast iron drill," And

REFRAIN:

Drill, ye tar - riers drill. And drill, ye tar - riers drill, For it's work all day for the sug - ar in your tay, Down be - hind the rail - way, And drill, ye tar - riers drill, and blast, and fire.

2 The boss was a fine man all around
But he married a lady six feet round.
She baked good bread, and she baked it well,
But she baked it hard as the holes of hell.

3 The new foreman is Dan McCann.
I'll tell you sure he's a blame mean man.
Last week a premature blast went off
And a mile in the air went big Jim Goff.

4 When pay day next it came around,
Poor Jim's pay a dollar short he found,
"What for?" says he, then came this reply,
"You were docked for the time you were up in the sky."

CHOICE OF BOB FLICK

The Wild Colonial Boy

pride of both his par-ents Was the wild co-lo-nial boy. So

REFRAIN *(In Tempo—Fast):*

come, all me hear-ties, We'll range the moun-tain side: To-

ge-ther we will plun-der, To-ge-ther we will ride. We'll

scour a-long the val-leys, And gal-lop o'er the plains, We

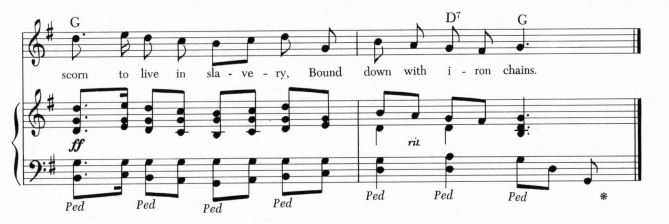

scorn to live in sla - ve - ry, Bound down with i - ron chains.

2   In sixty-one this darling youth commenced his wild career,
With a heart that knew no danger, no foeman did he fear.
He held up the Beechworth mailcoach and he robbed Judge MacEvoy
Who trembled and gave up his gold to the wild colonial boy.

3   One day as he was riding the mountain side along,
A listening to the little birds their pleasant laughing song,
Three mounted troopers came in view, Kelly, Davis and Fitzroy,
And thought that they would capture him, the wild colonial boy.

4   "Surrender now, Jack Doolan, you see there's three to one;
Surrender now, Jack Doolan, you daring highwayman!"
He drew a pistol from his belt and spun it like a toy.
"I'll fight but I won't surrender," said the wild colonial boy.

5   He fired at trooper Kelly and brought him to the ground,
And in return from Davis received a mortal wound.
All shattered through the jaws he lay, still firing at Fitzroy,
And that's the way they captured him, the wild colonial boy.

THE MITCHELL TRIO

A GREAT DEAL has happened during the ten years since I met the members of the Mitchell Trio. It's as if we have all passed through several generations, not just one decade. The sharp and stinging material the trio introduced, and for which they encountered hostility and censorship, are today "standards" of commentary songs. Much has happened, and the Mitchell Trio has helped to make it happen.

The threesome never set out to be folk singers or topical-protest singers. They wanted to be "free," in every sense of the word, to choose their own paths, musically and philosophically.

The last ten years saw them grow from gawky and unsure youths into self-assured and mature performing stars. I've learned a lot from Chad Mitchell, Mike Kobluk, Joe Frazier and John Denver. Mostly, I've learned about what it means to stick to one's guns, even in the heat of controversy.

This is what the Mitchells had to do, time and time again, in the early 1960s. "Twelve Days of Christmas" was a bitter rant against re-Nazification in Germany, and not a few people in production, television, concert management and elsewhere in show business said: "Take it easy, boys." "Don't rock the boat." "Why play against the house," or words to that effect. They stuck to their guns. Another song lambasted the John Birch Society mercilessly. Once again the boys stuck to their guns and kept singing.

The trio was formed in 1958 at Gonzaga University in Spokane, Washington, with the active patronage of Father Reinard Beaver of Gonzaga. With the priest serving as an unofficial manager, Chad, Mike and Mike Pugh worked their way across the country to New York, where they got a recording contract and started to sing on the Arthur Godfrey radio show. When Mike Pugh decided to return to Gonzaga, the search for a replacement began. The 152nd applicant was Joe Frazier. He got the job.

Several years of high excitement ensued. Tours and the college circuit were a demanding master. A trip through South America for the State Department was a post-graduate course in political science. Appearances with Harry Belafonte and recordings on Mercury added professional experience and success.

During the years, perspectives changed and so did personnel and finally the group's original name. Chad decided to try his hand at acting and solo singing. He left in 1965 to travel his own route and was replaced by John Denver. Joe Frazier and Mike Kobluk departed in 1967 and 1968 to be replaced by David Boise and Mike Johnson. With all the original members gone, the group was renamed Denver, Boise and Johnson. All the members of the group, past and present, have remained in touch with one another, and a Mitchell Trio alumni association occasionally gathers at my Manhattan studio.

The song choices for inclusion here show an amazing unanimity of interest in the British folk tradition. Mike Kobluk chose "Golden Vanity," an old sailing song. Joe chose the strong and beautiful "Bonny Streets of Fyvie-O," and John was attracted to "The Great Silkie" for its supernaturalism.

Left to right:
Joe Frazier,
Mike Kobluk,
John Denver

The Bonny Streets of Fyvie-O

Moderate March

It was a ___ troop of I - rish Dra - goons Come march - ing ___ down through ___ Fyv - ie - o And the cap - tain fell in love with a ve - ry bon - ny lass, And her name it was called ___ pret - ty Peg - gy O.

2   There's many a bonny lass in the town of Ochterlass,
There's many a bonny lassie in the geary-o,
There's many a bonny Jean in the streets of Aberdeen,
But the flure of them all is in FYVIE-O.

3   Oh, come doon the stair, pretty Peggy my dear,
O, come doon the stair, pretty Peggy-o.
Oh, come doon the stair, comb back your yellow hair,
Take a last farewell of your daddy-o.

4   It's braw, aye, it's braw, a captain's lady for to be,
It's braw to be a captain's lady-o.
It's braw to rave and rant, and follow with the camp,
And to march when your captain he is ready-o.

5   It's I'll gi' ye ribbons, love, and I'll gi' ye rings,
And I'll gi' ye a necklace of amber-o;
I'll gi' ye silken petticoats with flounces to the knee,
If you'll follow me doon to my chamber-o.

6   A soldier's wife I never shall be,
A soldier shall never enjoy me-o,
I never do intend to go to your foreign land,
And I never will marry a soldier-o.

7   The colonel cries, "Mount boys, mount boys, mount,"
But the captain he cries, "Tarry-o,
Oh, tarry for a while, just another day or twa,
For to see if this bonny lass will marry-o."

8   It's early next morning that we marched away,
And oh but the captain he was sorry-o,
The drums they did beat, how bonny they did beat,
And the band played bonny tunes of FYVIE-O.

9   It's long 'ere we went to old Melbern Toon,
We had the captain to carry-o;
And long 'ere we went into bonny Aberdeen,
We had the captain to bury-o.

10   Oh, green grow the banks of bonny Abenshire,
And low be the lowlands of FYVIE-O,
The captain's name was Ned, he died for a maid,
He died for the chambermaid of FYVIE-O.

The Golden Vanity

Low - land, Low - land, She sailed up-on the Low - land Sea.

2   Then up spoke our cabin boy, and boldly up spoke he,
And he said to our captain. "What will you give to me,
If I swim alongside of the Spanish enemy
And sink her in the Lowland, Lowland, Lowland,
And sink her in the Lowland sea?"

3   "Oh, I will give you silver, and I will give you gold,
And my own fair young daughter your bonny bride shall be,
If you swim alongside of the Spanish enemy,
And sink her in the Lowland, Lowland, Lowland,
And sink her in the Lowland sea.

4   Then the boy he made him ready, and overboard sprang he,
And he swam alongside of the Spanish enemy,
And with his brace and auger in her side he bored holes three,
And sank her in the Lowland, Lowland, Lowland,
And sank her in the Lowland sea.

5   Then quickly he swam back to the cheering of the crew,
But the captain would not heed him, for his promise he did rue,
And he scorned his poor entreatings when loudly he did sue,
And left him in the Lowland, Lowland, Lowland,
And left him in the Lowland sea.

6   Then roundabout he turned and swam to the port side,
And up unto his messmates, full bitterly he cried,
"Oh, messmates, draw me up for I'm drifting with the tide,
And I'm sinking in the Lowland, Lowland, Lowland,
And I'm sinking in the Lowland sea."

7   Then his messmates drew him up, but on the deck he died,
And they stitched him in his hammock which was so fair and white,
And they lowered him overboard, and he drifted with the tide,
And sank into the Lowland, Lowland, Lowland,
And sank into the Lowland sea.

The Great Silkie

Slow and Smooth

An earth - ly nour - ris sits and sings, And

aye she sings "Ba lil - ly wean,

Lit - tle ken I my bair - nis fa - ther, Far

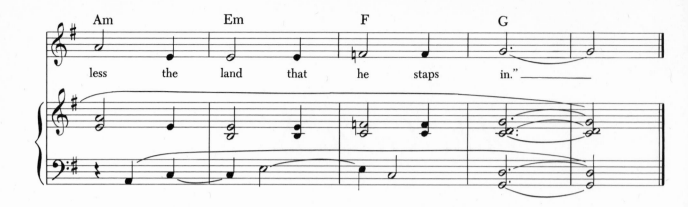

less the land that he staps in." _____

2 Then in steps he to her bed fit
And a grumley guest I'm sure was he
Saying, "Here I am, thy bairny's father
Although I be not comley

3 "I am a man upon the land
And I am a silkie in the sea
And when I'm far and far from land
My home it is in Sule Skerry."

4 "It was na weel," quo the maiden fair,
"It was na weel," indeed quo she.
"That the great silkie from Sule Skerry
Should hae come and aught a bairn ta me."

5 Then he has taken a purse of gold
And he has pat it upon her knee
Saying, "Gie to me my little young son
And take thee up thy nourris fee.

6 "It shall come to pass on a summer's day
When the sun shines hot on every stone
That I shall take my little young son
And teach him for to swim the foam.

7 "And thou shall marry a proud gunner
And a proud gunner I'm sure he'll be
And the very first shot that ever he'll shoot
He'll kill both my young son and me."

8 "Alas, alas," the maiden cried,
"This weary fate's been laid for me."
And then she said and then she said,
"I'll bury me in Sule Skerry."

DOC
WATSON

ONE OF the chronic oversimplifications we used to make was that country meant simplicity and city spelled complexity. To put the lie to that platitude, we present in evidence one complex country musician named Doc Watson. So complex, in fact, that Doc might be called one of the Renaissance men of country music, combining all the elements of rural music from folk to pop-country, with a few dashes of his own countrified sophistication.

Arthel (Doc) Watson established himself first on the urban scene as a guitar virtuoso, an incredibly dextrous technician who did such amazing things with finger-picking that the city folk fans lined up to study at the feet of the master. Beyond the subtlety of his shading, Doc Watson could execute a fast phrase with such clean articulation that it more resembled a run on a fiddle than a guitar. Such was his accomplishment with his instrument.

As time went on, however, the less apparent sides of his artistry began to surface, the brilliance and quickness of his mind, the vision that functioned behind his sightless eyes, the remarkable speed of his ear. Doc seemed to know about everything that was happening, just as it occurred.

Doc Watson was born forty four years ago in Deep Gap, North Carolina, son of a "pretty fair country picker." At the age of eleven, he got a fretless banjo made by his dad, and by seventeen he had managed to assimilate a great deal of music on records and radio.

Because rural people are much less concerned with authenticity of music than are the folklorists who study them, Doc became thoroughly eclectic in his listening and his performing, turning with equal affection to the classic folk song, the professional country music of old-time medicine and vaudeville shows, and finally the contemporary fusion of both, the Country and Western music centered in Nashville. As one of the liners on his Vanguard albums put it: "From all these musics, Doc has taken into his head whatever he found good, from authentic musical folklore, from professional re-workings of folk stuff, from the compositions of humble country amateurs and from the commercial music of the big cities...."

Doc Watson came to town with that inspired guide of rural artists, Ralph Rinzler. Ralph had encountered Doc about the same time he had first recorded Clarence "Tom" Ashley, in 1960, and they were all to become the darlings of the folk revival. Being younger and, in a sense, more versatile than Ashley, Doc was very much at home in the city folk world. He had a unique style, and a background completely different from that of the city folk singers, and he taught a lot to many of them. His singing had the fervor of the mountain uplands; his harmonica had the pungent wail of the open country; and that magical guitar had all that we have come to revere in great artists, folk or non-folk.

Tom Dooley

Adapted by "Doc" A.D. Watson
Copyright © 1965 by Stormking Music Inc.
All rights reserved. Used by permission.

132

left her by the road - side, then you hid her clothes and shoes.

2   You took her on the hillside for to make her your wife,
You took her on the hillside and there you took her life.

3   You dug the grave four feet long and you dug it three feet deep,
Your overcoat lay over her and tromped it with your feet.

4   I know they're gonna hang me, tomorrow I'll be dead,
Though I never even harmed a hair on poor little Laurie's head.

5   In this world and one more, then reckon where I'll be,
If it wasn't for Sherriff Grayson, I'd be in Tennessee.

6   At this time tomorrow where do you reckon I'll be,
Way down yonder in the holler hangin' on a white oak tree.

THE NEW LOST CITY RAMBLERS inspired a great renewal of interest in old-time string-band music. In fact, they were so good at re-creating this older style that they almost put themselves out of business.

Having done a fine job of building an audience, in cities and on campuses, for this old string music, they were to see a day when the audience would lean toward the original old-time sounds—the Tom Ashley band or the McGee Brothers—more than to the modern versions of their music by the New Lost City Ramblers. Although it pinched the Ramblers a bit, they knew that they had accomplished their mission in life—to stimulate today's appreciation of the music of another era.

The business never quite collapsed, however, because the Ramblers were a good draw wherever they went. And didn't they ramble, as the old song exclaims! Festivals and concerts and even into that posh parlor of sophistication, the Blue Angel. Some sort of cultural history was made with that engagement, back in June 1961, when the creaky, spiky, dancing counterpoint of fiddle, banjo and guitar was heard inside the smart Manhattan supper club.

The New Lost City Ramblers was formed in the autumn of 1958 by Mike Seeger, Tom Paley and John Cohen. These three had decided to build a band that adapted its style from the recordings of the 1920s and 1930s of such flavorsome hoary string bands as the Blue Ridge Corn Shuckers, the Fruit Jar Drinkers, the Buckle-Busters and even Dr. Smith's Champion Horse-Hair Pullers.

From such masters the Ramblers amalgamated a sound of scraping fiddle, banjo gallops, mandolin flights, dulcet Autoharp chords and, of course, the three voices riding above, under and right through the instrumental melee. This was true revival music, much as the Yerba Buena Jazz Band had revived New Orleans jazz and the Pro Musica Antiqua revived much of the fine music of the Renaissance and the medieval period.

Because the skilled musical archaeology of the New Lost City Ramblers extended to manner and style of wise-cracking and making patter, their shows were always a delight. Here, the citybilly truly met the hillbilly in artful burlesque of the country bands of old. After four years of musical barnstorming, Tom Paley left the Ramblers to pursue his photographic career in Europe, and he was replaced by the versatile singer and instrumentalist Tracy Schwarz.

A series of lovingly produced LPs on Folkways by the Ramblers brought the fun and the serious content of their music to many record collectors. The trio's repertoire seemed endless, from such romps as "It's a Shame to Beat Your Wife on Sunday" ("when you've got Monday, Tuesday, etc.") to the series of Depression songs that mirrored hard times in the country.

While remaining thus active with the Ramblers, John and Mike managed to carry on at least two careers apiece as collectors and organizers of old-time country music. Mike was nearly single-handedly responsible for the growth of an audience for Bluegrass in the cities, and John taped, photographed and wrote about such rural artists as Roscoe Holcomb of Kentucky. All the Ramblers played active parts with the group, Friends of Old-Time Music, for they were, in many ways, the genre's staunchest friends.

THE NEW LOST CITY RAMBLERS

Left to right:
Mike Seeger, Tracy Schwarz,
John Cohen

Lady of Carlysle

Down in Car - lysle there lived a la - dy,

Be - ing most beau - - ti - ful and gay.

She was de - ter - mined to live a la - dy, No

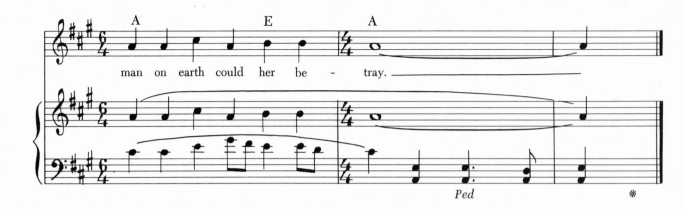

man on earth could her be - tray.

Ped ✻

2   Unless it was a man of honour,
A man of honour and high degree;
And there approached two loving soldiers
This fair lady for to see.

3   One being a brave lieutenant,
A brave lieutenant and a man of war.
The other being a brave sea captain,
Captain of a ship called *Hong Kong Kar.*

4   And then upspoke this brave young lady,
Saying, "I can't be but one man's bride;
If you'll come back tomorrow morning,
On this case we will decide."

5   She ordered her a span of horses,
A span of horses at her command,
And down the road these three together
Rode till they come to the lion's den.

6   And there they stopped and there they halted,
Those two soldiers stood gazing around.
And for the space of half an hour
That young lady lay speechless on the ground.

7   And when she did recover,
She threw her fan in the lion's den,
Saying, "Which of you, to gain a lady,
Will return my fan again?"

8   And then upspoke that brave lieutenant,
Raised his voice both loud and clear;
Says, "I know I am a true lover of women,
But I will not give my life for love."

9   And then upspoke that brave sea captain,
Raised his voice both loud and high;
Says, "I know I am a true lover of women
And I will return your fan or die."

10   Down in the lion's den he boldly entered,
The lions being both bold and fierce;
He walked around and in among them,
Did return her fan again.

11   And when she saw her true lover a-coming,
Seeing no harm to him was done,
She laid her head upon his bosom,
Saying, "Here's the prize that you have won."

Arkansas Sheik

If you do I'll tell you how it'll be, Cold corn - bread, mo - las - ses,

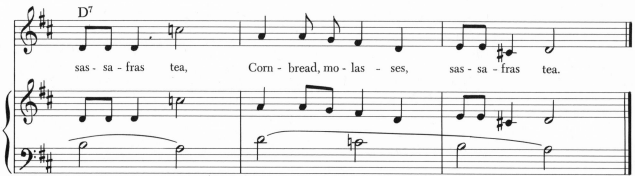

sas - sa - fras tea, Corn - bread, mo - las - ses, sas - sa - fras tea.

2 When you go a-courtin' I'll tell you how to dress,
A buckskin shirt, it is the best,
And a cloth hat more brim than crown,
An old pair of shoes with the heels run down,
Pair of shoes with the heels run down.

3 First thing he does whenever he comes in,
He takes a chew o' tobacco, slobbers on his chin.
First thing he says whenever he sits down,
"Gotta make a johnny cake, so bake it too brown.
Make a johnny cake, so bake it too brown."

4 You milk an old brindle cow and strain it in a gourd,
Put it in the corner and cover with a board.
Some gets a little and some gets a'none.
This is the way the Arkansas' run,
The way that the Arkansas' run.

5 An old board roof and an old wood floor,
An old cold bedstead, and old oak door,
Sleeping on the slats with a handful of straw,
Trying to get along with a mother-in-law,
Get along with a mother-in-law.

6 An old blind mule and an old milk cow,
Razor-back hog and bull tongue plow.
He had his pork salad and sassafras tea,
But the Arkansas sheik is a mystery to me,
Arkansas shiek is a mystery to me.

7 Well I sung you all my song
And I guess you find it's true,
The Arkansas sheik's feeling kind of blue.
He got drunk and he took off into town,
Arkansas gal turned his damper down,
Arkansas gal turned his damper down.

Rock About My Saro Jane

Fast

VERSE:

I've got a wife and five lit - tle chil - dren, Be - lieve I'll make a trip on the Big Mac - mil - lan, Oh Sa - ro Jane!

Oh, there's noth - ing to do but sit down and

sing And rock a - bout my Sa - ro Jane.

REFRAIN:

Oh, rock a - bout my Sa - ro Jane, Oh,

rock a - bout my Sa - ro Jane, Oh, there's

noth - ing to do but sit down and sing And

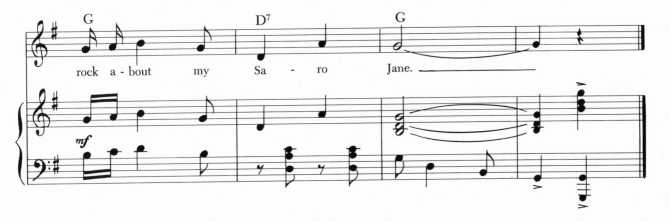

rock a - bout my Sa - ro Jane. _____

2   Engine busted and the whistle done blowed,
The head captain done fell overboard,
Oh Saro Jane!
Oh, there's nothing to do but sit down and sing
And rock about my Saro Jane.

3   Engine done crack and the whistle done squall,
The engineer fall through the hole in the wall,
Oh Saro Jane!
Oh, there's nothing to do but sit down and sing
And rock about my Saro Jane.

4   Yankees built boats for to shoot them rebels,
My musket's getting loaded and I'm going to hold her level,
Oh Saro Jane!
Oh, there's nothing to do but sit down and sing
And rock about my Saro Jane.

MALVINA REYNOLDS

SNOW on the roof doesn't mean that there's not fire in the furnace. Malvina Reynolds, at sixty-seven, still wields one of the most youthful typewriters and guitars in topical song.

The fact of Malvina's late-blooming musical career is one of the phenomena of the folk revival. The burst of creative energy from a woman who is a grandmother ought to prod a lot of us younger slouches into activity. But, as a long list of clever and unique songs will attest, Malvina doesn't just produce; she produces works of value, meaning and durability.

Should we mention a few titles to refresh your memory? Mal has written "Turn Around," "Little Boxes," "God Bless the Grass," "What Have They Done to the Rain?" and many more widely performed songs. Her works have been performed by most of the notable folk stars, and her special role has won this sort of comment: "The most unique songwriter in America. She refuses to give up on the human race." (Pete Seeger). "A gray-haired Joan of Arc" (Ralph J. Gleason).

Malvina turned to songwriting about twenty years ago, after an already full career as newspaper woman, mother and student. Living in Berkeley, California, she has seen a never-ending cycle of West Coast radical movements and been part of many of them. She is married to the soft-spoken Bud Reynolds, who turned from union-organizing to career-organizing with his wife.

Malvina's life has been dominated by nothing if not flexibility. Armed with a Ph.D., in Depression days she was unable to find teaching work, so plumbed other talents. With her waspish wit she moved into songwriting naturally, and soon she was also playing guitar and singing. When she admitted to a critic that she had a recurring frog in her throat, she added whimsically that it was unavoidable with all the atomic fallout in the atmosphere.

Malvina Reynolds is to the folk-song movement what Grandma Moses was to primitive art. On one of her recent Columbia albums was this comment: "[She] has a lot to impart to us all about youth and age, about . . . being 'fully alive.' . . . Her vigorous mind and spirit say: 'Start today, and don't worry about yesterday.' Her social commentary and compassion say that concern and rebellion are not just a phase of adolescent development on the way to complacent 'maturity.'"

So many of our clichéd thoughts about protest-topical songs must go out the window in the face of Malvina Reynolds. Because music is ageless and youth is ageless and spirit can endure, she tells us about renewal in a dynamic, creative way.

The traditional song that she has chosen is still another example of her ability to surprise. "Leatherwing Bat" is not the sort of song Malvina would write; it is the sort, however, she loves.

Leatherwing Bat

Fast and Rhythmic

VERSE:

"Hi," said the lit - tle   lea -ther-wing bat, "I'll tell you   the rea - son that,   The

rea - son that   I   fly by night   Is be - cause I   lost   my heart's de - light."

REFRAIN:

Tow - dy, dow - dy   did - dle - o   day,   Tow - dy, dow - dy   did - dle - o   day,

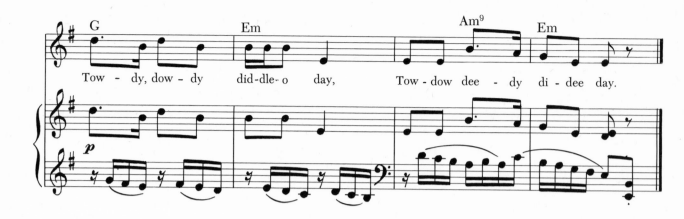

Tow - dy, dow - dy did-dle- o day, Tow - dow dee - dy di - dee day.

2 "Hi," said the blackbird, sitting on a chair,
"Once I courted a lady fair;
She proved fickle and turned her back,
And ever since then I've dressed in black."

3 "Hi," said the woodpecker, sitting on a fence,
"Once I courted a handsome wench;
She got scared and from me fled,
And ever since then my head's been red."

4 "Hi," said the little turtle dove,
"I'll tell you how to regain her love:
Court her night and court her day,
Never give her time to say 'O nay!' "

5 "Hi," said the blue-jay, as away he flew,
"If I was a younger man I'd have two.
If one was faithless and chanced to go,
I'd add the other string to my bow."

THE STAPLE SINGERS

ONE OF the many subdivisions of American folk music that sparks a special flame in listeners is Negro gospel song. Sophisticated listeners find the fire and fervor of gospel and its great voices a proud part of the folk tradition.

Dozens of gospel groups have been favored, but probably none more highly esteemed than the singing family group the Staple Singers. There was such kindness of spirit and virtuosity of performance among the father, two sisters and brother who made up the Staples that they began to be known as "the first family of gospel song."

Gospel song is a curious marriage of devotional lyrics and secular song, or, to condense, of religious ideas and worldly music. Although gospel has had a controversial history within the Negro church, as old hymns and spirituals gave way during the years to blues-based, jazzy rhythms and hand-clapping exuberance, modern gospel is by this time fully accepted, inside and outside the church.

While the Staple Singers can whip up a head of steam with hard "shouting gospel" they prove equally able to build excitement with understated, quietly pulsing songs. One can always distinguish the vocalism of the Staples, in its subtlety, its resonant harmonies, its sense of sure-footed rhythm and the syncopated hand-clapping that seems to give the beat new dimensions.

The story of the Staples is a typical one of growth through music and religion. Roebuck Staples was born in the poor bottom lands near Drew, Mississippi. In the midst of the Depression, the only escape route available for him and his wife, Oceola, was North, and they settled in Chicago. Pop Staples worked as a meat cutter by day, studied at night, and always sang in neighborhood church groups. The family grew with the births of Cleotha, Pervis, Yvonne and Mavis. By 1948 the children were old enough to start performing with their talented father, and their fame spread through the Negro district of Chicago and beyond.

By the time of the folk revival of the late 1950s the Staples had a strong reputation among folk fans. A little while later they made history by being the first gospel group to win the *Down Beat* International Jazz Critics Poll for the best vocal group. Folk and jazz festivals were clamoring for them, and they could always find an eager audience on their gospel-church circuit.

Although recordings have rarely been able to catch all the vibrant textures of the Staples, they were widely known through Riverside and Epic LPs. In such traditional songs as "Will the Circle Be Unbroken?", learned from Roebuck's centenarian father, or such modern compositions of their own as "Why Am I So Mistreated?", the hallmark of the Staples is quality. Pop gently uses a small amplified guitar that underlines rather than overwhelms the singing. Mavis's athletic, rich contralto shares the singing spotlight, as Cleotha and Pervis gently harmonize. There is the grit of the Mississippi soil in their harmonies along with a commandingly contemporary sound that appeals to a wide audience.

Although the Staple Singers (the family name is Staples) are professional performers, their identification with the loving, humanistic side of church work is deep. On the pillars of music and belief they build their career.

145

See That My Grave Is Kept Clean

One kind fa-vor I ask of you,

2   There's two white horses in a line,
There's two white horses in a line,
There's two white horses in a line,
Taking me to my burying ground.

3   Have you ever heard that coffin sound?
Have you ever heard that coffin sound?
Have you ever heard that coffin sound?
Lord God, you'll know I'm dead and gone.

4   Have you ever heard them church bells tone?
Have you ever heard them church bells tone?
Have you ever heard them church bells tone?
Lord God, you'll know I'm under ground.

Swing Low, Sweet Chariot

2 If you get there before I do,
Coming for to carry me home,
Tell all my friends I'm coming too,
Coming for to carry me home.

3 The brightest day that ever I saw,
Coming for to carry me home,
When Jesus wash'd my sins away,
Coming for to carry me home.

4 I'm some-times up and some-times down,
Coming for to carry me home,
But still my soul feels heavenly bound,
Coming for to carry me home.

Steal Away

Very Slow

REFRAIN:

Steal a - way, steal a - way, steal a - way, to Je - sus!

Steal a - way, steal a - way home. I ain't got long to stay here.

VERSE:

My Lord — He calls me, He calls me by the thun - der: The

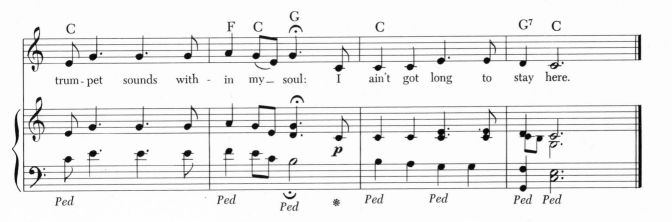

trum - pet sounds with - in my — soul: I ain't got long to stay here.

Ped   Ped   Ped   *   Ped   Ped   Ped Ped

2 Green trees are bending,
Poor sinners stand trembling;
The trumpet sounds within my soul:
I ain't got long to stay here.

3 My Lord calls me,
He calls me by the lightning;
The trumpet sounds within my soul:
I ain't got long to stay here.

4 Tombstones are bursting,
Poor sinners are trembling;
The trumpet sounds within my soul:
I ain't got long to stay here.

Paul Stookey

Peter Yarrow

Mary Travers

PETER, PAUL AND MARY

I STILL find it difficult to think of Peter, Paul and Mary as world-famous performers, wealthy and successful people. I remember them in the months of their first rehearsals in Mary's walk-up apartment on MacDougal Street in Greenwich Village—or sitting on the floor of my Eleventh Street apartment, strumming, singing, learning.

I must confess that for some time I didn't think they would be successful. In fact I tried to persuade two other arrangers to work with them before I "resigned" myself to helping.

Although as their musical director I was supposed to teach them, in the years we've worked together I have learned much from them. Their unwillingness to accept "you can't do that because it breaks the XYZ rule of harmony" allowed us to find new and strong sounds. I learned to accept, and look for, dissonances that vocal groups had not used before. They would work for hours to get one note in one part.

Sometimes the time was wasted. But occasionally they found an extraordinary new way of harmonizing a melody. The inner harmony part of "I gave her my heart but she wanted my soul" at the end of "Don't Think Twice, It's All Right" took a full day to work out, but it's as arresting an harmonic phrase as any I've ever heard.

The very strong guitar-accompanying style of Peter and Paul, I feel, is unique. They expanded

what was accepted as guitar accompaniment to a much fuller and more musical level.

Our rehearsals have never been dull. Often they have been stormy, because they are three strong individuals with three different personalities. It is difficult enough these days to think for oneself let alone for a group. But Peter, Paul and Mary have done it for years now. They have achieved a harmony of thinking onstage and off that has given them a unique status.

Inevitably, each of my three colleagues and friends had a different song to suggest for the collection. I told them that all nine members of the New Christy Minstrels could agree upon one song, and they thought about that a few minutes. Then they suggested the following three songs. If I had given them more time, it might have turned into three dozen.

Mary Travers' choice is "Sometimes I Feel Like a Motherless Child," the classic spiritual. Paul Stookey chose "The Minstrel Boy," the stirring Irish song, and Peter Yarrow elected "On Top of Old Smoky," the hill-country song that keeps weaving itself into the fabric of American folk tradition.

152

On Top of Old Smoky

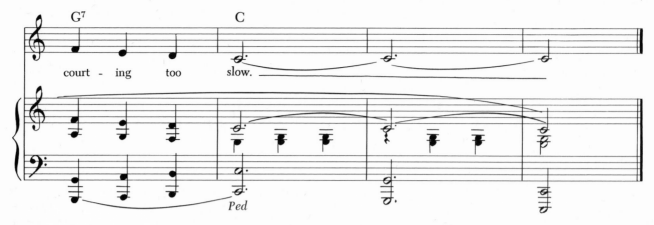

court - ing too slow.

Ped

2   Now courting is pleasure, and parting is grief,
And a false hearted lover is worse than a thief.

3   A thief will just rob you and take what you have
But a false hearted lover will lead you to the grave.

4   And the grave will decay you and turn you to dust
Not one boy in a hundred a poor girl can trust.

5   They'll hug and kiss you and tell you more lies
Than the cross-ties on the railroad or the stars in the skies.

6   So come all you young maidens and listen to me
Never place your affection on a green willow tree.

7   For the leaves they will wither and the roots they will die
You'll all be forsaken and never know why.

8   On top of Old Smoky all covered with snow
I lost my true lover from courting too slow.

The Minstrel Boy

Moderately Slow

The Min - strel Boy — to the war is gone, In the ranks of death —— you'll find him; His fa - ther's sword — he has gird - ed on, And his wild harp slung — be - hind him. "Land of song!" said the

war - rior bard, "Tho' all the world be - trays _____ thee, One
sword, at least _ thy _ rights shall guard, One _ faith - ful harp _ shall _ praise thee!"

2   The minstrel fell! but the foe man's chain
Could not bring his proud soul under;
The harp he lov'd ne'er spoke again,
For he tore its chords asunder,
And said, "No chains shall sully thee,
Thou soul of love and bravery!
Thy songs were made for the pure and free,
They shall never sound in slavery!"

Sometimes I Feel
Like a Motherless Child

2 If this was judgment day,
If this was judgment day,
If this was judgment day
Ev'ry little soul would pray.
Ev'ry little soul would pray.
True believer, ev'ry little soul would pray.
Ev'ry little soul would pray.

3 Sometimes I feel like I'm almost gone,
Sometimes I feel like I'm almost gone.
Sometimes I feel like I'm almost gone.
'Way up in the heavenly land.
'Way up in the heavenly land.
True believer, 'way up in the heavenly land.
'Way up in the heavenly land.

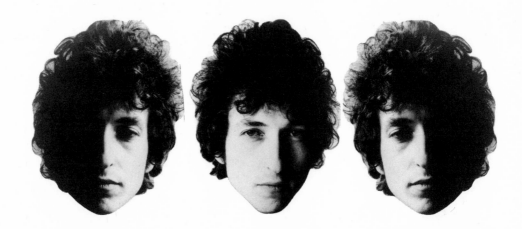

BOB DYLAN

BECAUSE he has been so frequently involved with the *avant-garde*, with innovation, with shock and with new frontiers, it is quite easy to forget that Bob Dylan has returned time and time again to the continuing music of tradition.

At the very height of the Dylan controversy of 1965, when he turned into a rock-'n'-roll musician, in a form called folk-rock, he reiterated his love of traditional music. Because of past narrowness and a genuinely purist view that had so dominated American folk circles, Dylan had to take another pledge of allegiance to traditional music before many would grant him the moral right to play electric rock music.

Those of us who were always sympathetic and interested in the latest trend that Dylan would produce knew that forward movement for him did not necessarily mean a rejection of what he had done before. To anyone who knew Dylan's work closely, the prism of folk tradition, pop tradition, country tradition, blues tradition and the tradition of the *avant-garde* were keystones for his own change. He

has been compared to a Picasso, running hell-bent through a dozen modes and styles, eclectic and electric, saying what he chose to say before saying it a different way, philosophically and musically and lyrically again.

Bob Dylan is a major figure in American culture of the 1960s. He is important in a variety of ways: as writer, performer, singer, composer, stage figure, rebellion symbol. He was to become a superstar, breaking out of the confines of the folk audience and the pop audience. He was to have a bigger following than that, and a lot of people thought he was more important than either the folk revival or the pop movement that followed it. Whatever your terms of relative importance of creative people, Bob Dylan was, is and will remain important.

That Bob chooses a bad-man song is no surprise, and that he chooses one that Woody Guthrie also chose to convert into "The Ballad of Tom Joad" is no surprise either. Robert Shelton, long at work on a critical biography of Dylan, pointed out in *The New York Times* that Dylan has been fascinated all his life with the loser, the drop-out, the outsider and the rebel. The bad man, in reality and in fantasy, interested Dylan from his own first scuffling days around Greenwich Village till "John Wesley Harding" and beyond. It was romanticism that drew Dylan to the outlaw-hero, but it was also a belief that things are not always what they seem: Sometimes the outlaw was more a man of integrity than the so-called man of the law.

159

John Hardy

2 John Hardy was standing in the dice-room door,
He was not concerned in the game;
Rozella threw down one silver dollar,
Saying, "Deal John Hardy in the game, poor boy!"
Saying, "Deal John Hardy in the game."

3 John Hardy threw down one half-dollar,
Saying, "One half of this I'll play,
And the man that wins my money this time,
I'm going to blow his life away,
And lay him in his lonesome grave."

4 John Hardy was making for the station that night,
It was so dark he could hardly see;
A policeman took him by the arm,
Saying, "John, won't you come and go with me, poor boy?
John, won't you come and go with me?"

5 Every station they passed through,
They heard the people say,
"Yonder goes John Hardy making his escape,
John Hardy is getting away, poor boy!
John Hardy is getting away!"

6 They brought John Hardy out before the judge,
And bond they offered him;
No bond was allowed a murderin' man,
So they put John Hardy back in jail, poor boy!
They put John Hardy back in jail.

7 John Hardy had a father and mother,
He sent for them to go his bail.
No bail was allowed for murderin' a man,
So they shoved John Hardy back in jail, poor boy!
So they shoved John Hardy back in jail.

8 Johnny Hardy was standin' in his cell,
With tears runnin' down his eyes,
"I've been the death of many a poor man,
And now I'm ready to die, O Lord,
And now I'm ready to die.

9 "I've been to the east and I've been to the west
I've been this wide world round,
I've been to the river and I've been baptised,
So take me to my hanging ground, O Lord,
So take me to my hanging ground."

JOAN BAEZ

THAT special singer Joan Baez has become almost the personal embodiment of the folk revival. It seems that we were all eighteen with her, grew up with her, changed with her and her recordings, from "Silver Dagger" to "Yesterday."

It is probably unfair to single out anyone in our gallery of singular performers. So we'll just say that Joanie is special—for her pure voice, her unquenchable social conscience, her unshakable belief in social action, even if it spells a month in jail for herself.

Can it really be as long ago as 1959 that Joan Baez came on the scene at the Newport Folk Festival? Can it be almost a decade since the writers were saying of her: "a folk-song Joan of Arc," "the Callas of folk song," "the darling of the urban folk scene"? Can it be so long ago that she was as much the young symbol of the Newport Festival as Pete Seeger had been the symbol of an earlier era?

Those early recordings and concerts by Joan were to set a style for the urban revival of the 1960s: the long hair, the quiet and loving demeanor that preceded the flower children by at least six years, and the stress on expert vocalizing and musical control. But, as with many of the figures of the folk scene, Joan was more than just a singer. She stood for something then and stands for something today.

It began easily, quietly, with a teenage protest against an air raid; then it attained its musical expression with a protest against the pollution of our air by radioactive material. Gathering strength, Joan became increasingly identified with a movement against violence of all sorts, establishing a school for the study of non-violence at her home in Carmel, California.

With her mentor and friend, Ira Sandperl, she toured Europe and the American South, doing whatever she could to fight discrimination and violence. When the Free Speech movement developed on the campus of the University of California at Berkeley, Joan was called upon to sing and speak. When the anti-draft and anti-Vietnam War movements developed on the West Coast, Joan and her mother demonstrated their deep commitment by spending a month in jail in early 1967.

Her dedicated social action was the more effective because of her complete seriousness and dignity as a concert artist and recording musician. Musically and socially Joan Baez became a totally involved young woman, using her art to extend the beauty of her idealistic belief. Inspiring countless thousands of admirers, she took her place near Pete Seeger in believing that folk song and social action are two expressions of that belief.

All My Trials

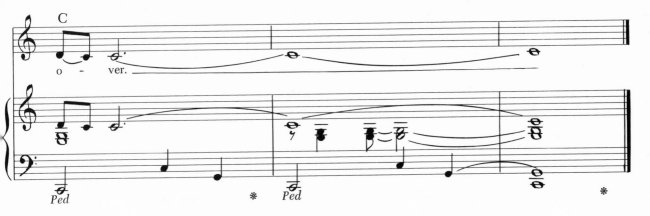

2 I had a little book, 'twas given to me,
And every leaf spelled victory,
All my trials, Lord, soon be over.

3 If religion was a thing that money could buy
The rich would live and the poor would die,
All my trials, Lord, soon be over.

4 The highest tree in Paradise
The Christians call the Tree of Life,
All my trials, Lord, soon be over.

5 The Jordan River is chilly and cold,
The chill and cold does chill my soul,
All my trials, Lord, soon be over.

IAN AND SYLVIA

HOW WIDE a compass of performing style there is in folk song! It is as valid for a Bukka White to sing in a raspy, gruff voice as it is for Ian and Sylvia to unreel long velvety ribbons of the smoothest, highly polished tones.

The Canadian-American duo may achieve a refined elegance in their singing, but they are among the most knowledgeable workers in folk tradition, or contemporary song, or country music, or the blues. Not only is the bulk of American folk song in their purlieu, but also the traditions of Canadian music and the songs that they have written themselves. One need only mention some of the couple's compositions to demonstrate their distinctive approach to modern folk song: "Four Strong Winds," "Loving Sound," "So Much for Dreaming" and many others.

Their performances are intelligent, poised and controlled. Ian and Sylvia are also striking in their physical attractiveness, which enhances the beauty of their work.

Long, lean, Ian Tyson was born in 1933 in British Columbia and reared on a small farm there. As a young man he earned his way with a variety of jobs, from migratory worker to lumberjack and rodeo performer. He graduated from the Vancouver School of Art and worked as a commercial artist until he began to realize that his first love was music.

He met Sylvia Fricker in Toronto in 1959. She was born in Chatham, Ontario, and learned music from her mother, who was a teacher, choir leader and organist. Sylvia went on to teach herself guitar and Autoharp and became a first-class folklore hunter, intrigued with all the European and native influences that were found in Canadian song. Ian and Sylvia started singing together in 1960 and were married three years later.

Their ensemble style has developed over the years into something quite unlike any other folk duet. The interplay of harmony and rhythm is refined to a high brilliance. Although each may take a solo role, they are a combination in which each vocal and instrumental element plays a vital part.

Their compositions are as strikingly original as their ensemble sound. Ian is a poet of the Canadian landscape, intrigued with the distances, the loneliness, the sweep of the countryside. Sylvia has found inspiration in Negro gospel and blues, and yet manages to cast them into a form that is completely her own.

In concert, their own work is done along with songs in many different folk idioms. They may sing a classic Anglo-American-Canadian ballad, a French-Canadian nationalist song, a spiritual, with equal understanding, depth and finesse.

Their professional careers have followed the usual paths, with little that is startling or dramatic. Rather, they are hard-working, earnest professionals, constantly developing their craft.

When First Unto This Country

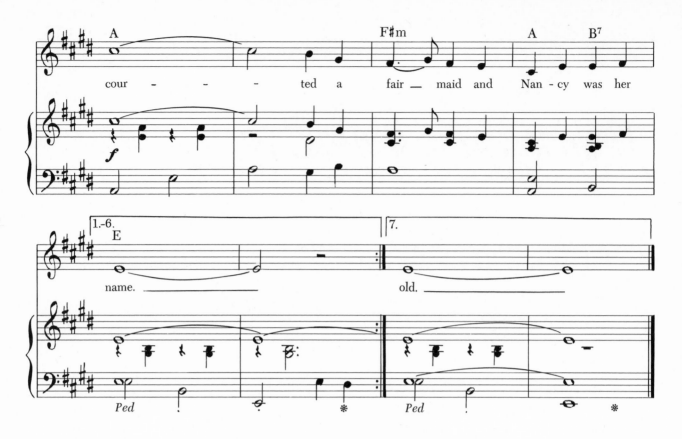

cour- - - -ted a fair — maid and Nan-cy was her name. _____ old. _____

2 I courted her for love, and her love I didn't obtain.
Do you think I've any reason or right to complain?

3 I rode to see my Nancy, I rode both day and night,
Till I stole a fine gray horse from Captain William White.

4 The sheriff's men, they'd followed and overtaken me,
They carted me away to the penitentiary.

5 They opened up the door and they shoved me in,
And they shaved off my head and they shaved off my chin.

6 They beat me and they banged me and they fed me on dry beans,
Till I wished to my own heart I'd never been a thief.

7 With my hands all in pockets and my cap put on so bold,
And my coat of many colors, like Jacob of old.

Handsome Molly

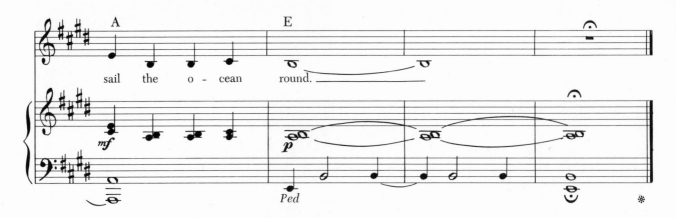

sail the o - cean round. ____

2 While sailing on the ocean,
While sailing on the sea,
Think of Handsome Molly
Wherever she might be.

3 Don't you remember, Molly,
You gave me your right hand?
Said if you ever marry
That I would be the man.

4 I'll go down to the river,
While everyone's asleep
Think of Handsome Molly,
And then lay down and weep.

CAROLYN HESTER

ALL TOO RARELY in the competitive business of music we find a performer whose warmth and graciousness are so real that we can almost forget music is a business.

Carolyn Hester is such a person. We have watched her grow up from a young Texas girl into a woman, without losing her freshness or honesty.

Carolyn arrived in New York in 1956 to study acting with the American Theater Wing. She had already done one LP, "Scarlet Ribbon," before the revival started going in earnest, and she went on to record for Tradition, Dot and Columbia. She had early experience in moving about; after her birth in Waco, Texas, her family wandered to Dallas, Austin and Denver. Her first professional appearance was at the age of thirteen on a Texas television station. Her family had a wide range of musical interests, but it was folk song and the music of Burl Ives that first attracted her.

From New York in those exciting days of the late 1950s Carolyn soon was traveling everywhere: Folk City, Yale's Indian Neck Festival, Newport, the Showboat in Washington, the Gate of Horn in Chicago.

After her marriage to the late Richard Fariña, Carolyn was to become as well known in Britain as she was in America. She appeared at the Edinburgh Festival twice, was a regular on British television and one of the first of the American girl folk stars of England. Looking for a fresh-faced, long-haired beauty to symbolize the folk boom, *The Saturday Evening Post* chose Carolyn's picture for a cover.

Although Carolyn was among the many persons drawn to folk song solely by an affinity for the music, soon she was involved with the many social causes that were linked to the folk movement. She saw the South with wiser eyes when she went to Mississippi on several "freedom sings." Carolyn had also been one of the organizers of the singers' boycott of ABC-TV's "Hootenanny" when that show refused to allow Pete Seeger to perform.

The song Carolyn Hester has chosen is a gem of folk-lyric. Another version was known as far back as the eighteenth century by the title "Waly, Waly." This beautiful fragment is part of a long Scots ballad, "Lord Jamie Douglas," and like many of the old ballads has a classic dignity about it. Says Carolyn of "The Water Is Wide": "I sing this almost every time I perform. It is so reassuring and relaxing to me, I am able to warm up on it. It's no surprise that this beautiful, classically beautiful, song was transplanted to America and has survived for centuries."

171

The Water Is Wide

two   And both shall row,   my love and   I.

2 Oh, waly, waly, up the bank,
And waly, waly down the braes,
And waly, waly by yon burnside,
Where me and my love was wont to go.

3 I leaned my back against an oak,
I thought it was a trusty tree,
But first it bent and then it broke,
And so did my false love to me.

4 When sea and sand turn far inland,
And mussels grow on every tree—
When cockle shells turn silver bells,
Then my false love will be true to me.

5 Oh love is handsome, love is fine,
Love is a jewel when it is new.
But when it's old it turneth cold
And fades away like morning dew.

LONG BEFORE anyone was turning from folk songs to contemporary "art" songs, a few members of the community were simply converting traditional music into an art music. Not formally. Not with fancy or outlandish arrangements. The conversion to art song was accomplished subtly, by the addition to

JUDY COLLINS

simple folk song of the depth of understanding of a variety of the other arts.

A leading practitioner of this has been Judy Collins, one of the first miners of folk melody, who went deep below the surface and came up with some new material or some new exploration to report on. Judy can imbue a simple song with color and drama. Yet—and here is the special magic—she leaves the work intact, in substance and meaning, as it was in tradition. That is an art.

Her background was as a classical performer. Born in Seattle and reared in Denver, Judy was the daughter of a blind radio personality whose shows

offered, in her words, "a potpourri of philosophy, piano and good music." Judy studied piano and became something of a child prodigy, appearing with the Denver Businessmen's Symphony. Eleven years of constant absorption with piano finally led Judy to discard, for a time, the big instrument in favor of a beat-up steel guitar her father had given her. Soon she was haunting the folk dens of Denver, a lively area where Eastern and Western folk movements met and happily coexisted. To *Time* magazine Judy defined the links: "Folk music became my contact with other human beings, a way of saying what I think is happening inside their souls. . . ."

Many people have criticized young folk singers who seemed to be singing of trouble without knowing it. Judy sadly had been through a rough growing-up period in which personal trouble was no stranger. This gave her a special ability, it seemed to many in her audience, to probe into pain and feeling where it was beyond the reach of many younger, more sheltered performers.

Nothing so characterized Judy's stretching years in the folk world as that quality of reaching and trying new areas, new material, new interpretive side roads, new accompaniments. All of this made her a highly rounded and flexible performer, one capable of surprising her audiences. She surprised us by going folk-rock one moment and singing Brecht and Weill the next. She helped promote and popularize the works of Leonard Cohen long before he arrived on the scene to sing the songs himself.

Judy Collins stands for an intelligence and maturity in folk song that is not what one always associates with such a youthful person. For that, she has always enjoyed the respect of her peers and the honor of her audiences. "The Cruel Mother," and Anglo-Scots-American song about infanticide, is one of the most stark and chilling ballads in world folklore. Judy Collins' performance of it is one the listener will never forget.

The Cruel Mother

Very Slow

There was a la - dy lived in the north, Oh the rose ___ and the Lin - zie - o. ___ She fell in love ___ with her fa - ther's clerk, Down ___ by the Green-wood si - die o.

2 She loved him up and she loved him down,
Oh the rose and the Linzie-o.
She loved him till she filled her arms,
Down by the Greenwood sidie-o.

3 She placed her foot against an oak,
Oh the rose and the Linzie-o.
First it bent and then it broke,
Down by the Greenwood sidie-o.

4   Then she placed her foot against a thorn,
Oh the rose and the Linzie-o.
There those two little babes were born,
Down by the Greenwood sidie-o.

5   She pulled a knife both keen and sharp,
Oh the rose and the Linzie-o.
She thrust those two little babes to the heart,
Down by the Greenwood sidie-o.

6   She buried those two little babes under a marble stone,
Oh the rose and the Linzie-o.
Thinking this would never be known,
Down by the Greenwood sidie-o.

7   One day, sitting in her father's hall,
Oh the rose and the Linzie-o,
She spied those little babes playing ball,
Down by the Greenwood sidie-o.

8   "O babes, O babes, if you are mine,
Oh the rose and the Linzie-o,
I'll dress you up in silks so fine,
Down by the Greenwood sidie-o."

9   "O mother, when we were thine,
Oh the rose and the Linzie-o,
You never dressed us up in coarse nor fine,
Down by the Greenwood sidie-o.

10   "Now we are up in heaven to dwell,
Oh the rose and the Linzie-o,
And you are doomed to hell,
Down by the Greenwood sidie-o."

THE NEW CHRISTY MINSTRELS

ONE OF the reasons that some recording companies and some coffeehouse owners loved the folk revival was the unending source of cheap talent afforded by the singer-songwriter-guitarist-banjoist-one-man-band. Although often cloaked in high-sounding phrases and the most noble of stated intents and purposes, the reawakening of interest in folk music was aided by the fact that it very definitely provided more economical talent than the rock 'n' roll booms did.

But strange things began to happen in the folk scene that even got out of the control of economy-minded entrepreneurs. After a variety of soloists or self-accompanied singers, the trios and the quartets lost their novelty and the concept of the folk chorale became established. Helping to set this pattern and becoming the seed bed for several subsequent folk chorales was the New Christy Minstrels, nine or sometimes ten cheerful, bouncy well-scrubbed and well-trained group singers.

The name of the group, which was organized by one Randy Sparks, was derived from a group that had begun back in 1842. The original Christy Minstrels, led by Edwin P. Christy, were in business largely to popularize the material of Stephen Foster, and they also had the corniness of early vaudeville and the inevitable blackface minstrel make-up that dominated the pre-Civil War entertainment business.

The New Christy Minstrels, however, were a different kettle of fish, as the exigencies and demands of 1961 were quite different. Mostly, the group of seven boys and two girls that Sparks organized was trying for a warm and lighthearted approach to folk arrangements. Nothing heavy, nothing very perplexing, nothing too taxing to performer or to audience. And it was just such a successful formula that led the group to a command appearance at the White House, to being the first American folk group with a commercial recording distributed in the Soviet Union, and, of course, a rattlingly successful life on American TV and recording and the college concert circuit.

For a time the New Christy Minstrels became a rough-and-tumble proving ground for many young West Coast singers. It afforded them a chance at steady work and income while they set plans or pursued ideas for solo careers. The best-known alumnus of the Minstrels is probably Barry McGuire. But whatever the personnel changes or the new faces in the Minstrels, the group identity managed to remain the same happy blend of simplicity and good cheer.

With firm direction and a knowledge that they are filling a particular need in a particular area of entertainment, the Minstrels keep rolling along.

The Group, 1968

The Big Rock Candy Mountain

In the Big Rock Can - dy Moun - tains, it's a land that's fair and bright, The hand - outs grow like bush - es, __ and you sleep out ev - 'ry night; The box cars all are emp - ty and the sun shines ev - 'ry

179

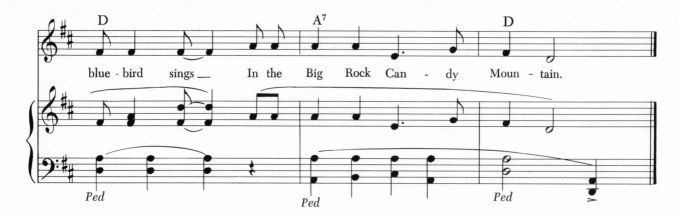

blue - bird   sings __   In the   Big   Rock   Can - dy   Moun - tain.

2   In the Big Rock Candy Mountains you never change your socks,
Little streams of alky-hol comes trickling down the rocks.
Oh the shacks all have to tip their hats and the railroad bulls are blind
There's a lake of stew
And gingerale too
And you can paddle all around it
In a big Canoe
In the Big Rock Candy Mountain.

3   In the Big Rock Candy Mountains the cops have wooden legs,
The bull-dogs all have rubber teeth and the hens lay soft-boiled eggs.
The box-cars all are empty and the sun shines every day.
I'm bound to go
Where there ain't no snow
Where the sleet don't fall
And the wind don't blow
In the Big Rock Candy Mountain.

4   In the Big Rock Candy Mountains the jails are made of tin,
You can slip right out again as soon as they put you in.
There ain't no short handled shovels, no axes, saws nor picks.
I'm bound to stay
Where you sleep all day
Where they hung the jerk
That invented work
In the Big Rock Candy Mountain.

THE SERENDIPITY SINGERS

THE SUCCESS of the New Christy Minstrels proved that there was a place in America's bustling music world for the folk chorale. It afforded the flexibility, variety and full-ranging settings that were beyond the capabilities of the already proven folk trios and quartets.

Many groups derivative of the New Christies were formed, but the one that was to be the most durable and popular was the Serendipity Singers. Musical values were only one factor in the making of this chorale of seven young men and two girls. Attention to appearance, costuming, even choreography were all stressed, with the aim of presenting a wholesome, attractive group of American youth.

Musically, the Serendipities chose the path of "free choice," from a traditional folk song to a recent pop tune, from topical ditties to show tunes. The instrumentation and over-all approach put the group in the folk category, but the music and style were not easy to place in any one class. "Serendipity," incidentally, refers to the old myth of the Three Princes of Serendip and has been defined as "the sudden coming upon a happy event when least expected." So it is with the music of the Serendipity Singers, wheeling free from "Don't Let the Rain Come Down" to "Beans in My Ears" to jazz tunes or show material or the satiric song bag of Shel Silverstein.

The group was the outgrowth of a collegiate folk trio, formed at the University of Colorado by Bryan Sennett with Brooks Hatch and Mike Brovsky. Not content with the potential of a trio's sound, they added Bob Young, a bass player, John Madden and Jon Arbenz, guitarists, also students at Colorado.

To bring the group up to its present strength of nine, three more musician-singers came from Texas: Lynne Weintraub, Tommy Tieman and Diane Decker. But there was nothing especially regional or Western about the group, for it really simmered up to its polished professionalism at the Greenwich Village coffeehouse the Bitter End. There the club's owner, Fred Weintraub, stepped in, as did its musical director and arranger, Bob Bowers.

The rest is a story of hard work, travel and an ever-broadening circuit, from colleges to the ABC "Hootenanny" show and a featured place on the NBC-TV "Today" show, from tours to Australia and Canada to recurring appearances at its home, the Bitter End. The repertory of this nine-member group is also ever-widening, including material that has a jazz flavor. And they have developed set pieces that touch on satire and light comedy, such as their "New Frankie and Johnny Song," "Sobbin' Women" and "Whale of a Tale."

To anyone who knows the off-stage problems and debates of even folk trios or quartets, the continuing harmony and rapport of the Serendipity Singers is a minor marvel. If they give the appearance on stage of enjoying every minute of what they are doing, it can be considered a fairly good approximation of the group's spirits. They are even a cohesive enough group to have picked, without long parliamentary delay, a favorite traditional folk song for inclusion in this collection.

181

Let Me Fly

REFRAIN:

Now let me fly, _____ now let me fly. _____ Now let me fly __ to Mount Zi-on, Lord, Lord. _____

2 I got a mother in the Promised Land,
Ain't gonna stop till I shake her hand.
Not so particular 'bout shakin' her hand.
Just want to go to the Promised Land.

3 Meet that hypocrite on the street,
First thing he'll do is to show his teeth.
Next thing he'll do is to tell a lie,
And the best thing to do is to pass him by.

BUFFY SAINTE-MARIE

ONE OF the fruitful by-products of the American folk revival has been the unearthing of "lost" or submerged minority cultures within the over-all fabric of American folk culture. One of the most submerged has been that of the Indian, whose music, ritual and lore were of course, here long before the coffeehouse folk fad.

Several singers of Indian descent tried their best to focus attention on what was artistic and lasting in their backgrounds, most notably Johnny Cash, the late Peter La Farge, Patrick Sky and Buffy Sainte-Marie. This last artist was to become notable not only because of new interest in Indian lore but also through her own sophisticated and exotic style of singing and songwriting.

This very beautiful girl, with her torrents of dark hair and striking clothes, came on the folk scene about 1963. She was born in Maine of Cree Indian parents who traced their family lines back to Saskatchewan in Canada. But the simple life of a rural Indian was not for her, and she ended up studying education and Oriental philosophy at the University of Massachusetts, where she graduated with honors.

Her first public appearances were made while she was a college senior and it did not take long before a near cult was forming around her. Everything about Buffy's manner and material radiated excitement and originality and the stamp of a strong new personality. When she sang her blistering indictment of "Cod'ine," one knew that here was a forceful new voice on the songwriting roster. Whether her subsequent songs spoke of topical matters, militarism ("Universal Soldier") or discrimination against Indians, it was always with a fresh point of view and an avoidance of the clichés that early crept into the topical songwriting movement.

Her singing has gone through many transformations, not all of them totally satisfying to some discriminating listeners, who fear that some melodrama is replacing her initial dramatic impact. Whatever the merits of that debate, when Buffy Sainte-Marie addresses herself to one of her two hundred songs, one can always be sure that there will be great power and passion.

Buffy's grounding in both Indian and white American traditional music is secure. She startled many when she fused these elements into an eerie and arresting innovation by humming into a mouth bow to augment her own singing. Although a "primitive" Indian folk custom, it was not to be widely essayed or imitated, because few could hope to surpass Buffy's skill on the rare instrument.

Buffy's own recordings on the Vanguard label, have enjoyed great popularity, while her songs have been recorded by many others, from Odetta to Donovan. For this collection Buffy has chosen a song of English origin, "Must I Go Bound," that has numerous versions. The poetry of the lyrics is among the most refined to be found in any folk-art collection, as deft and subtle as the most polished work of a classical poet.

Must I Go Bound

Smooth and Moderate

Must I go bound while you go free? Must I love one who won't love me? Must I then act the child-ish part, And love the one who'd break my heart?

2 I put my finger to the bush
To pluck a rose of fairest kind,
The thorn it pierced me to a touch,
And so I left the rose behind.

3 I leaned my back against an oak.
I thought it was a trusty tree,
But first it bent and then it broke,
Just as my love proved false to me.

4 Oh, I'll go bound while you go free,
And I'll love one who won't love me,
And I will act the childish part,
And love the one who'd break my heart.

DAVE VAN RONK

DAVE VAN RONK looks like an unmade bed. Or, if that comparison is not dignified enough, he might be compared to the lion in *The Wizard of Oz*, leading his audiences down a fanciful yellow-brick road to lands unknown. But when it comes to singing, the bluesman extraordinary wails and soars like a winged tiger.

Van Ronk is typical of certain commanding folk performers who never quite became "stars," yet whose hold on an audience is always sure. Their influence on other musicians is equally strong. The burly New Yorker is thus one of our leading musicians' music-makers. He has been making keen statements, verbally and musically, since the late 1950s.

One of the distinctive elements of his singing is the rough-edged rasp and growl of the country blues, an arresting sound that wins instant attention. But this is no primitive technique, for one of the remarkable things about the Van Ronk growl is that he has so much control over it, making it plaintive or strutting at will. The Van Ronk guitar is an integral part of his performance, and he makes as cunning a use of the instrument as we have heard in the last decade.

Dave was born in New York in 1936. His first love was jazz and he started playing jazz banjo. He later became interested in the blues, all kinds, and soon he was re-creating the harsh and soulful sounds of the Mississippi Delta, the East Texas piney woods, the flatlands of the Carolinas.

No element of Van Ronk's work has proved more controversial than the question of whether a white singer can perform Negro music. Dave's work is a convincing answer to the doubters. This debate had long raged in jazz circles and it was to rage again in the folk community. Nationalists felt that Negro music was best made by Negroes, while others said that such a superb body of traditional songs could be performed by anyone who appreciated it, regardless of background.

Although Van Ronk was working within the elements of a Negro style, he quickly translated it into a music that had relevance and meaning for white, middle-class urban youth. Dave Van Ronk is probably responsible for teaching more white city kids the substance and the kernel of the blues than any performer in America. (Ironically, another white blues master, Alexis Koerner of London, was to help lay the musical basis for the later rhythm and blues movement in Britain. Like Van Ronk, he never attained personal stardom, just star billing for the music he loved so well.)

Dave has been a sought-after guitar teacher, a frequent performer on the coffeehouse and concert circuit, and has been recorded on many labels. For a time he and Sam Charters were heading a sparky little revival jug band, which recorded for Mercury, and appeared at the Village Vanguard. When Van Ronk sings "Poor Lazarus" or "House of the Rising Sun," when he struts his guitar gem, "St. Louis Tickle," when he probes the involved world of the blues, he is a master interpreter.

Sprig of Thyme

Come — all you sweet and — fair young maids Who — flou-rish in your prime, — Be — sure and keep your — gar-den clean, Let — no man take — your

2 In June comes in the primrose flower,
But that is not for me.
I will pull off my primrose flower,
And plant a willow tree.
Oh, willow, green willow,
With sorrow mixed among,
To tell to all this wide wide world,
I here loved a false young man.

MANY talented performers barely have one career. Glenn Yarbrough has enjoyed two careers, and he's still going strong. Glenn was the anchor man of the Limeliters, one of the most successful of the early pop-folk groups. Philosophic differences, varying personal aspirations and battle fatigue led to the break-up of the Limeliters, with Lou Gottlieb and Alex Hassilev going their own ways. Glenn went his way and found himself with another life as a singer, better known than ever before.

It happened almost by accident. Glenn wanted to rest after the ardors of concert work and traveling. He was perhaps the most easygoing of the three Limeliters, and he figured that there was enough money in the bank to warrant a long and leisurely cruise, from San Francisco to the Caribbean on his boat, the *Armorel*. Before setting sail, he cut an album, "Time to Move On"—a prophetically titled work, by the way—and it got off to such a rapid start that Glenn nearly never got to make the cruise. Before he had a chance to realize what had happened he was enjoying a new career as a solo performer.

Glenn had helped set the original title for his group when he started his career at the club in Aspen, Colorado, called the Limelite. To many it was Glenn's first-rate, warmly lyrical singing that was the great contribution of the group.

Beyond the straightforward and appealing singing that characterized Glenn's second career in pop and folk music, he was clearly trying to say a few things that no one else of comparable stature was saying. He was advocating a sort of poetic freedom and honesty that was represented by the work of Rod McKuen. Glenn helped McKuen achieve the enormous popularity he currently enjoys. In the notes to his album "For Emily, Wherever I May Find Her," Glenn took note of the dual revolutions of our time, led by Negro civil-rights activists and by youth "against hypocrisy and stupidity, against established concepts and precepts that have failed in the past. . . . For mankind, very close to destruction, salvation seems to be emerging in the young. . . . I find myself an unwilling spectator during a great struggle, but somehow we will join hands and I will be proud to sing their song."

We applaud his words but don't agree that Glenn is a spectator. When an artist enunciates the good and clean and meaningful art that Glenn Yarbrough does in his singing, he is no spectator. He is part of the battle, using the weapons he knows best.

GLENN YARBROUGH

Nine Hundred Miles

2 Well this train I ride on
Is a hundred coaches long,
You can hear the whistle blow a hundred miles,
And the lonesome whistle call
Is mournfullest of all,
'Cause it's nine hundred miles from my home,
And I hate to hear that lonesome whistle blow.

3 Well, I'll pawn you my watch
And I'll pawn you my chain,
I'll pawn you my gold diamond ring,
If that train runs me right,
I'll be home tomorrow night,
'Cause I'm nine hundred miles from my home,
And I hate to hear that lonesome whistle blow.

Swannanoa, N. C.
Nov. 16, 1967

Dear Milton,

AFTER thinking about your question for a long time, I am convinced that I don't have any one folk song from tradition that is my favorite.

For one reason, I grew up to age 16 in the coal camps of West Virginia and there isn't much tradition in the camps. The main diet of music is hillbilly and church gospel. I think I heard "Froggie Went a-courtin'" and a couple of popular things like this and that is about it.

I really discovered folk music by going away from the mountains. At Warren Wilson College I was introduced to folk tales by someone wanting me to memorize one and tell it at a party, which I did. It was a collection of "Jack Tales" by Richard Chase. Later on I met Mr. Chase, a folk character himself, and told some of the tales to him that he had collected, to his great amusement and satisfaction. (He approved of how I shifted details to my own liking and embellished the characters with my own words and imagination.)

Mr. Chase drug me about the mountains with him on many occasions looking for tales and songs. I remember responding to a beautiful song called the "Turtle Dove." It was very lyrical, minor and struck some sensitive chords in me. There are many versions, as you know, but his is the most beautiful. One verse says:

> 'Oh don't you see yon crow flyin' high
> Shall turn his color white
> Before that I'm in the arms of my true love
> Bright noon shall turn to night, my love
> Bright noon shall turn to night.'

It may or may not surprise you to hear that there is a lack of tradition in the mining towns, especially the short-lived ones. People come and go without really settling roots. There are many foreigners fresh from the old country. There is a Negro population which unfortunately I never got to know musically, or even very personally. A Negro man used to come to our church in the evening and teach us shape note singing.

Later on I discovered the world of folk music on record through Susan Reed, Burl Ives and on down the list. I responded very strongly to classical music in some simple music appreciation classes. Later on I collected a great many tapes of mountain people singing old ballads, many of them gory, many with beautiful melodies, all of them tending to be sad.

The only musical training I ever had was one semester of voice with Miss Gladys Jameson of Berea, a master collector and arranger of folk music. She was a very inspiring woman and seemed to know the soul of a folk song. I used some of her ideas in a poem, which I'm including in a brochure called "The Music Teacher." The one line: "A thought can set a sound in motion" I know came from her. The only thing that prevented me from having a very deep and lasting relationship with her was that she didn't put much stock in my own desire for song writing and self-expression. This is often true with purists and traditionalists, they don't want you to alter one word. So eventually I gave up the weekly lesson and went my own way.

I must admit that I've had a guilty conscience about song writing because of these various elements of tradition. Pure people wouldn't allow me to sing at their festivals, for fear I'd slip in an original composition. Then the city people rejected me because I wasn't barefoot and twangy, authentic. Also some folk fans associated me with the Kingston Trio. In some part I've been a man without an audience, a personal, meaningful audience. However, it is changing now. I sing a lot of concerts in the Appalachian area, colleges and fairs, and I've always had a certain loyal audience. Also some of the traditional people gradually mellowed toward me. In the folk scene, Judy Collins and some others helped me by recording my songs. Things are much better now.

During the early, frustrating years I also got stung by the *Little Sandy Review* when I brought out my first album on Monitor. "Billy Edd: U.S.A." They said it was some of the weakest song writing they'd ever heard, plus I was a fake, not a folk singer, but somebody who ought to try out for Curly in *Oklahoma*.

Unfortunately they had a lot to be critical of. The songs were too young and weak, the guitar work most unexciting and the record was produced for a total of $250.00, about 15 songs. There was at least one good song on the album, though, or two: "Farewell Brother" and "Ain't Goin' Home Soon," about the coal mines. So it wasn't a total loss, but it sure got me off to a shaky start as a folk singer and composer and I don't think Monitor sold very many records.

I seem to be giving you more than you asked for, so I'll shut up.

Good luck with your book, and I'm sorry I can't give you a more direct answer to your question about my favorite traditional song.

Sincerely,

Billy Edd Wheeler

Thanks to a fertile pen, or in this case a fluent typewriter, Billy Edd Wheeler has told us his own story. His letter, I feel, is worth quoting *in toto* because it reflects some very damaging, very destructive elements that have been at work in some areas of the folk-music world. When you add to these problems the long-standing pressures of commercial show business, you can understand how some young talents have been crushed between the two problems. Fortunately, Billy Edd Wheeler has strong talent and strong fiber. He will survive.

BILLY EDD WHEELER

Turtle Dove

Now don't you see a lit-tle tur-tle dove Sit-ting

un - der a mul - ber - ry tree? _____ See

how that _ she doth _ mourn her true love, As

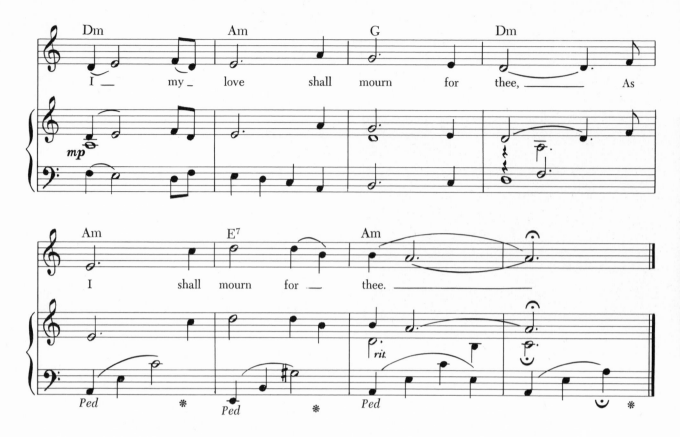

2   Now fare thee well, my little turtle dove, oh fare thee well for a while,
For tho' I go I will surely come again
If I go ten thousand miles, my dear, if I go ten thousand miles.

3   The crow that's black, my little turtle dove, doth change its color white,
E'er I prove false to the maiden that I love,
The noon day shall be night, my dear, the noon day shall be night.

4   The hills shall fly, my little turtle dove, the roaring billows burn,
E'er I prove false to the maiden that I love,
Or I a traitor turn, my dear, or I a traitor turn.

194

THE SMOTHERS BROTHERS

Tom Smothers

EVERYONE loves the guy down the road who can laugh us out of our seriousness, who can make us stop taking ourselves so weightily. When there are two guys down the road like that, we really prize them, particularly in the folk-music field where we do get serious rather often.

This has been one of the delightful side effects of having Tom and Dick Smothers around. In the old days they kept the folk revival from being too stiff and solemn. In recent days they have kept it from being an historical oddity by hosting the brightest, and most popular and controversial, new TV show in many seasons.

When the Smothers Brothers first came to light back in the early 1960s, they were rather droll pop-folksters who were regarded more as comedians than musicians. Tom played the fool and Dick played the patient, sensible partner. It worked, as Tom poked fun at long scholarly introductions to simple songs and plagued his brother about the whole guitar-bass-melody seriousness. In their rendition of "Michael, Row the Boat Ashore," for instance, Tom halts the music to shout: "Hey, Michael, you'd better get that boat back; you'll lose your deposit"; or gently inverts the traditional line to read: "Black is the color of my love's true hair."

For the ethnic-pomposity set, the whimsy of the Smothers Brothers was a tonic and a caution. For the general listener the Smothers Brothers were sheer delight.

Smothers Brothers fans were delighted in early 1967 to find the duo in charge of a Sunday-night TV variety show. Little did even the boys' greatest admirers suspect that before long the "Smothers Brothers Comedy Hour" would be not only challenging the impregnable popularity of "Bonanza," but fast becoming the most popular show on American television.

Along the way, Tom and Dick stuck to their guns and remained folk singers with anti-Establishment ideas. They were the first commercial, sponsored show to offer Pete Seeger on American television, and they made a point of bringing him back to sing the entire lyrics for "The Big Muddy" after CBS had excised the song on a previous appearance.

The censors at CBS had never taken quite such a drubbing from any comics as they received from Tom and Dick. On the show and off, the Smothers Brothers were infusing new life and vitality into the concept of TV free speech. And, skillfully, they used their clashes over having a free hand from the censors to help promote the show with the burgeoning youth audience. Speaking out against the Vietnam war and the Federal Administration became as much a part of the TV show as their variety guests and their own performing.

The Smothers Brothers stand for a new health in American TV, just as they were "a force for good in the community" of folk song. Oh, yes. They sing and play folk songs very, very nicely.

Dick Smothers

The Fox

Fast

The fox went out on a chil- ly night, — Prayed for the moon to give him light, — He'd man- y a mile to go that night Be - fore he reached the

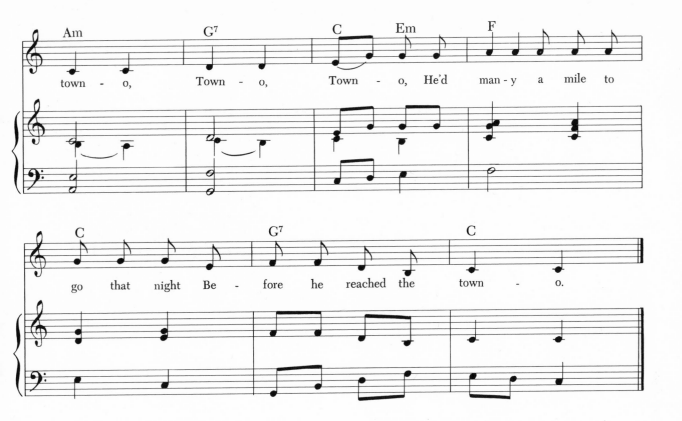

town - o, Town - o, Town - o, He'd man-y a mile to go that night Be - fore he reached the town - o.

2 He ran till he came to a great big pen
Where the ducks and the geese were put therein,
"A couple of you will grease my chin
Before I leave this town-o,
Town-o, Town-o,
A couple of you will grease my chin
Before I leave this town-o,"

3 He grabbed the gray goose by the neck,
Throwed a duck across his back;
He didn't mind their quack, quack, quack,
And their legs all dangling down-o,
Down-o, Down-o,
He didn't mind their quack, quack, quack,
And their legs all dangling down-o.

4 The old mother Flipper-Flopper jumped out of bed,
Out of the window she cocked her head,
Crying, "John, John, the gray goose is gone,
And the fox is on the town-o,
Town-o, Town-o."
Crying, "John, John, the gray goose is gone,
And the fox is on the town-o."

5 Then John, he went to the top of the hill,
Blowed his horn both loud and shrill;
The fox, he said, "I better flee with my kill
Or they'll soon be on my trail-o,
Trail-o, Trail-o."
The fox, he said, "I better flee with my kill
Or they'll soon be on my trail-o."

6 He ran till he came to his cozy den,
There were the little ones eight, nine, ten.
They said, "Daddy, better go back again
For it must be a mightly fine town-o,
Town-o, Town-o."
They said, "Daddy, better go back again
For it must be a mighty fine town-o."

7 Then the fox and his wife without any strife,
Cut up the goose with a fork and knife;
They never had such a supper in their life,
And the little ones chewed on the bones-o,
Bones-o, Bones-o.
They never had such a supper in their life,
And the little ones chewed on the bones-o.

PHIL OCHS

IS THERE a more logical progression in occupations than the step from journalism to topical songwriting? Malvina Reynolds took that step, and Pete Seeger was thinking of becoming a newspaper reporter before he turned to folk song. Phil Ochs was a journalism student when the idea of writing singing editorials occurred to him.

Although he has moved from bright and urgently topical songs into themes of more durability, such as "There but for Fortune," Phil perhaps made his greatest impact as a "troubadour of the New Left." His "living newspaper" was kept up to date in the early 1960s with fresh editions of "The Ballad of William Worthy," "Talking Vietnam Blues" and "I Ain't Marching Any More."

Phil was, for a time, very much a product of the *New York Broadside* school of topical songwriting, speaking out on dozens of current issues with his joggy melodies, his biting and sarcastic lyrics and his tart wit. He found, at that stage, that much of what he had learned about journalism applied as well to the writer of topical songs—the need to keep on top of the news, to form clear opinions and to state them with an eye toward persuasiveness and interest-holding, and the deadlines, for even he was forced to admit that "nothing is deader than yesterday's newspaper."

But Phil Ochs, showing a strong ability to shift the style and the content of his writing, is as alive as tomorrow's newspaper. Of late, his work has probed in the direction of greater psychological depth and evaluations of middle-class life.

Phil Ochs is a smiling, articulate resident of Greenwich Village. He reads everything, likes all styles of music and all sorts of provocative, thinking people. He is very much in touch with the youthful, sophisticated world of the campus as well as that of the

198

hippies, but travels, as do most artists, alone.

Although Phil told an interviewer once "I was born in Moscow in 1917," he was, in fact, born in El Paso in 1940, the son of an Army medical officer. He graduated from Staunton Military Academy, an experience that presumably led to his staunch anti-militarism.

After studying the classical clarinet, Ochs was drawn to the folk scene through his friend at Ohio State University, Jim Glover, now of the singing duet Jim and Jean. A foretaste of the controversies that lay ahead of Phil, he was banished to being the university newspaper's music reviewer after writing a pro-Castro article.

In Cleveland, contact with Bob Gibson and John Winn further affected Phil's musical style and solidified his plan of moving to New York. For a time he was a regular at the shabby little Third Street pass-the-basket club, The Thirdside. But it was a place in which to sharpen the thrust of his satiric commentaries. Recording on Elektra, Phil moved into the larger concert circuit and was often called on to whip up enthusiasm for student demonstrations. A singer and writer still very much in evolution, the Phil Ochs of tomorrow may bear little resemblance to the Phil Ochs of yesterday. He is, as the title of the song he chose, "Lang A'Growing."

Lang A' Growing

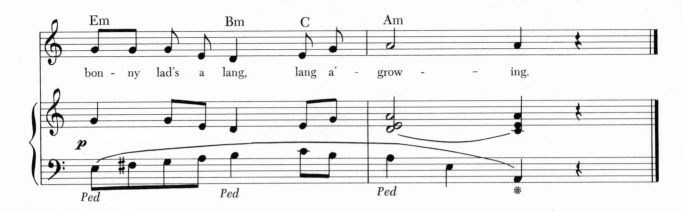

bon - ny lad's a lang, lang a' - grow - - ing.

2 "Oh father, oh father, I fear you've done me wrong,
You've married me to a bonny boy, but I fear he is too young!
For I am twice twelve and he's but thirteen,
My bonny lad's lang, lang a'growing."

3 "Oh daughter, oh daughter, I've done you no wrong,
I've married you to the rich lord's son,
And he will make a lord for you to wait upon;
He's young but he's daily a'growing."

4 "Oh father, oh father, if you see fit,
I'll send him to college for one year yet.
I'll bind a blue ribbon all about his hat,
To let the maids know he is married."

5 As I looked down from my father's castle wall,
There I saw the boys a-playing of the ball.
My own true love was the flow'r of them all,
He's young, but he's daily a'growing.

6 I made him a shirt of the finest of lawn,
And sewed it all with my own lovely hand,
And with ev'ry stitch the tears came flowing down:
He's young, but he's daily a'growing.

7 At the age of thirteen he was a married man;
At the age of fourteen, the father of a son;
At the age of fifteen his grave it was green,
And that put an end to his a'growing!

TOM PAXTON

ALL OF our "angry young men" aren't necessarily angry in their posture toward life. Tom Paxton, for one notable example, is a singularly benign person with an easygoing temperament. But, as some of his songs and many of his statements reveal, Tom is a "concerned" human being, a social critic, one of those people who think twice about the *status quo*.

The "protest song" side of Tom Paxton's musical personality has enriched our contemporary folk tradition. Having learned much from the work of his fellow-Oklahoman, Woody Guthrie, and from Pete Seeger, Paxton knows that humor is a valuable weapon. This has given some of his best songs the double edge of satiric bite along with honest statement. "Lyndon Johnson Told the Nation," "The Talking Viet Nam Pot Luck Blues," "What Did You Learn in School Today?" and "I Read It in the *Daily News*" are examples of his best sardonic protest.

But this is only part of his prolific creative outpouring. Such songs as "The Last Thing on My Mind" and "Can't Help but Wonder Where I'm Bound" are personal romanticism in the very best American folk tradition. An inspired melodist, Tom has written many songs whose tunes, once heard, are difficult to forget.

Tom Paxton attended Drama School at the University of Oklahoma and continued his studies with his guitar and the Burl Ives songbook. He did some post-graduate work with the Army at Fort Dix, and some "field work" at the Gaslight Cafe in Greenwich Village. Then he married Midge Cummings, a pert young lady to whom we give thanks for many of Tom's best love songs.

I first met Tom during auditions to replace Mike Pugh for the Mitchell Trio. I was dubious about his potential with the group, but after working with him for a few days I began to realize what a strong writing talent he had. He failed the audition but it led to a personal relationship in which we became close friends and co-workers.

Tom is active on many creative levels. He is doing the music and lyrics of a dramatization of the life of Thoreau, is working on an American folk opera and a novel. And he continues to record regularly for Elektra. His light and jolly tune "Bottle of Wine" was high on the hit charts in its version by the Fireballs. "The Last Thing on My Mind," in a Country version by Porter Wagoner and Dolly Parton, also was a big hit in 1968. It has already been recorded all over the world forty times.

201

Off to Sea Once More

Fast, Rollicking

When first I land-ed in Liv - er - pool, I went up - on a spree. ___ Me mon - ey at last I spent ___ it fast, Got drunk as drunk could be. ___ And when me mon - ey it was ___ all gone, 'Twas

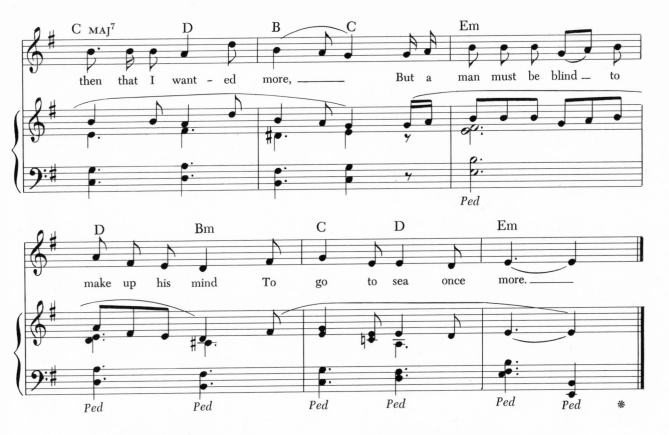

then that I want-ed more, _____ But a man must be blind _ to

make up his mind To go to sea once more. _____

2   I spent that night with Angeline
Too drunk to roll in bed
Me watch was new and me money was too
In the mornin' with them she fled.
And as I walked the streets about
All the whores how they did roar,
"There goes Jack back, the poor sailor lad
He must go to sea once more."

3   Now as I walked the streets about
I met with Papa Brown.
I asked him for to take me in
And he looked at me with a frown.
He said, "Last time you was paid up
With me you'll chalk up no score
But I'll give yez a chance and take your advance
And send you to sea once more."

4   He shipped me on board of a whalin' ship
Bound out to the Arctic Seas
Where the cold winds blow in the ice and snow
And Jamaica rum will freeze
And worse to bear no hard weather gear
For I'd lost all me money ashore.
'Twas then that I wished that I was dead
And would go to sea no more.

5   Some days we caught you whales, me lads
Some days we caught you none
With a twenty foot oar stuck in your hand
From four o'clock in the morn
And when the shades of night come on
You rest on your weary oar.
'Twas then that I wished that I was dead
Or safe with the girls ashore.

6   Come all ye salt seafarin' lads
And listen to my song
When ya come off them hard weather trips
I'd have yez not go wrong.
Take my advice, drink no strong drink
Don't go sleepin' with no whore
But get married lads and have all night in
And go to sea no more.

A LOT OF criticism has been lodged against the past decade's crop of folk singers, some justified, some quite unfair. One vulnerable area of the folk movement that rarely is attacked is a tendency for singers to become so serious that they lose their sense of humor if, indeed, they ever had one.

No one can ever say that about the whimsical Patrick Sky. He seems to enjoy a joke, however corny, almost as much as a song. There's a touch of Will Rogers, a dash of W. C. Fields, and for some added folk flavor a bit of Rambling Jack Elliott in Pat Sky's stage antics. Of course, these are only ingredients in his comedy style, and he is very distinctly an individual.

Patrick has been something of a novelty on the urban folk scene—a real country boy, with the drawling speech, the easy manner, the unhurried pace of the old South. He was born twenty-five years ago in Liveoak Gardens, Georgia, and reared near the LaFouche Swamps of Louisiana. Country and Western and folk music were part and parcel of his early years. In 1965 he drifted into New York looking for life experience and work experience. He found a lot of both.

The curious admixture of his folk-singing grandmother with his hip-speaking Village contemporaries resulted in what was, for Pat and his growing legion of admirers, the best of both worlds. His singing and writing of songs and comedy material reflected his earlier world and his new milieu. His 'Separation Blues" and sardonic "I Don't Want You Hangin' Round" caught the full sweep of his wit. But this was no clown, and some of his serious songs clearly expressed his involvement. These included "Many a Mile," with which Buffy Sainte-Marie titled her second album, "Nectar of God" and "Love Will Endure." Because of the contrast to his light side, Patrick's serious songs seemed to stand out in even bolder relief.

He worked over the Village club circuit, soon had an enthusiastic following on campuses and at festivals. Vanguard recorded him, and he did solo concerts at Town and Carnegie Halls. He got his first chance at films with a small one, "Down the Road," a documentary urging conservation, for which he did the narration and supplied the music, including a specially composed song, "Beautiful Beach."

Patrick Sky is quite proud of his Indian ancestry and has repeatedly identified himself with various Indian rights activities. Mostly, though, he is an individualist, simply concerned with music and anecdotes that spring from no particular place or time. He is at ease in the city and the country and to many of us has resembled a sort of young Andy Griffith who one day will be popping up on a TV series as a somewhat sophisticated "country boy."

For this collection Patrick chose that roistering old folk tune "Jay Gould's Daughter." He recorded it in his own special fashion on his second Vanguard album, "A Harvest of Gentle Clang." Jay Gould, it may be recalled, was one of the famous railroad "robber barons" of the nineteenth century, and as to his legendary daughter, turn to the song.

PATRICK SKY

Jay Gould's Daughter

Early one morning it began to rain, 'Round the corner came a passenger train. On that train was Hobo John, He's a

good old round-er but he's dead and gone. He's dead and gone,— he's

dead and gone. — He's a good old round-er but he's dead and gone. —

2 Charlie Snyder was a good engineer,
Told the fireman not to fear,
Pour your water, boys, shovel on your coal,
Stick your head out the window, see the drivers roll.
See the drivers roll, see the drivers roll,
Stick your head out the window, see the drivers roll.

3 Jay Gould's daughter said before she died,
One more road I would like to ride,
Tell me daughter, what might it be,
The Atchison, Topeka and the Santa Fe.
The Santa Fe, the Santa Fe,
The Atchison, Topeka and the Santa Fe.

4 Jay Gould's daughter said before she died,
Two more drinks I would like to try,
Tell me daughter, what might they be,
A glass of water, hot cup of tea.
Hot cup of tea, hot cup of tea,
A glass of water, hot cup of tea.

GORDON LIGHTFOOT

No ONE would want to rob Canada of its special identity among nations. And yet so much of Canadian culture bears a brotherly, or cousinly, relationship to our own that we can feel right at home with Canadian performers.

No Canadian performer has made himself quite so much at home in the United States as Gordon Lightfoot, a visitor from up north who has crossed not only the Canadian border but also the borders between country and folk and pop music.

Gordon has the sort of relaxation that is a hallmark of country performers, whether of Nashville or of Toronto. His hearty, warm baritone lingers over a melody like a cowpoke leaning over the top rail of a corral. His fingers are at home on the fingerboard of a guitar the way a cowboy is at home in a bunkhouse.

Gordon Lightfoot was born and reared in Orillia, Ontario, the town that was later to get on the folk map with a lively folk festival of its own. He dates his first performing back nearly twenty years ago, when, at the age of five, he sang at a Kiwanis Festival. High-school days saw him in plays and operettas as well as singing and playing drums with a dance band. For a year thereafter he studied at the Westlake College of Music in Hollywood.

While then capable of developing musically in any of several directions, Gordon settled on a job as studio singer and dancer on a Canadian Broadcasting Corporation show, "Country Hoedown." This led ultimately to a BBC television stint as host, in London, of eight one-hour "Country and Western" shows. More TV experience followed in Canada with solo appearances on "Nightcap," "Take Thirty" and "A La Carte." Naturally, he appeared on Oscar Brand's series, "Let's Sing Out."

During the work on the London show, Gordon turned to songwriting and has, in four years, racked up quite an impressive catalogue of songs. The Peter, Paul and Mary hit "For Lovin' Me" and Marty Robbin's "Ribbon of Darkness" were both written by Lightfoot. Along with the songs of Ian Tyson and Sylvia Fricker, Gordon Lightfoot's work is part of the new and expanding body of song that has helped give Canadians a strong role in the folk revival.

Lightfoot has appeared at The Newport Folk Festival and has given a solo concert at Manhattan's Town Hall. His personality on stage is strong, virile and yet curiously understated and modest throughout. He seems to offer the sort of restrained self-composure so often seen in highly talented performers. He has no need to shout, because he feels he has something of musical and poetic validity to say.

For this collection Lightfoot has chosen the Newfoundland folk song "Harbour Le Cou."

Harbour Le Cou

As ___ I rowed a - shore from my schoon - er close by,
A girl on the beach I did chance to es - py.
Her hair it was red and her

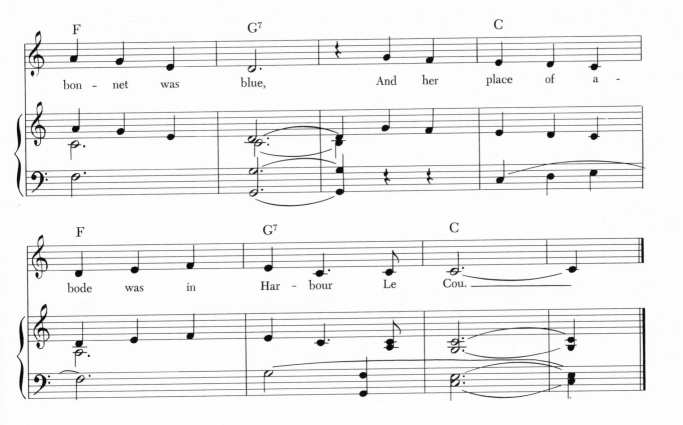

bon - net was blue, And her place of a -
bode was in Har - bour Le Cou.

2 Now boldly I asked her to walk on the sand,
She smiled at me gaily and held out her hand.
So I buttons me gurnsey and I hove way me chew
In the dark rolling waters of Harbour Le Cou.

3 And as we strolled along at the close of the day
I thought of my wife who was back in Tore Bay.
I knew that she'd kill me if only she knew
I was courtin' a maiden in Harbour Le Cou.

4 As we passed an old lighthouse at the head of the shore
I met an old comrade I'd sailed with before.
He treated me kindly, said, "Bill, how are you?
It is seldom we see you in Harbour Le Cou."

5 And as I was parting, this maiden in tow,
He broke up my party with one single blow.
"Say hello to your missus and wee kiddies too.
I remember her well, she's from Harbour Le Cou."

6 Then I looked at this maiden a-standing 'long side.
Her jaw it did drop and her mouth opened wide.
And then like a she-cat, upon me she flew
And I fled from the furies of Harbour Le Cou.

7 Come all you young sailors who walk on the shore,
Beware of old comrades you've sailed with before,
Beware of the maiden with the bonnet of blue,
And the pretty young damsels of Harbour Le Cou.

209

ERIC ANDERSEN

AFTER some of the excesses of the 1963 "hootenanny" fad, it was feared that the appearance of so much able new urban talent might not be repeated. But still the young American singers came.

Among the latest of significant new singing and songwriting talent is a lean and romantic figure named Eric Andersen. Eric arrived in New York at about the same time that the Beatles were making their first splash in America, but long hair was the only apparent similarity.

Eric came into New York City from upstate New York, a blue-jeaned young rambler with stories about riding boxcars and hopping freights. Beyond the stories were some intensely burning songs that were clearly derivative—of Dylan and Paxton and others—but Eric's individual style shone through the influences.

And there was an individuality of statement as well. Eric spoke of physical passion and of sexual love ("Come to My Bedside, My Darlin'") in a way that the folk singers had not sung for a long time, if ever. He seemed, at first, to believe in an emotion that was far from voguish in the early 1960s—love. (It's been only a few short years since hate and anger and protest in our new music have followed Eric's lead.)

210

Eric was not limited to a single attitude or style. In "The Hustler" he began to strike out against those he felt were turning life into nothing but a buying-and-selling game. He reached an even higher expression with his widely recorded song "Violets of Dawn," a fireworks show of poetic imagery.

For a time Eric became deeply involved with the civil-rights movement, journeying to the Mississippi back country only a short while after Goodman, Cheney and Schwerner had been killed for their civil-rights activity. But though Eric's sensitive observations were leading him to his own conclusions, he was still not afraid to ask questions, in person or in such songs as "The Bumblebee"—questions that were deeply disturbing because they challenged so many cruel answers.

He was to reflect the early 1960s in finding that self-discovery was of greater appeal than public activism.

He held a Town Hall audience spellbound with a brilliant concert that showed how well he could work with the backing of electric instruments. In many ways Eric worked into folk-rock easily and quickly. The strength of the instrumental backing pushed him forward and freed him for more interpretative depth.

Eric Andersen is proving to be not a brief sensation but an important and growing artist of originality and depth.

For this collection he has chosen "The Butcher Boy."

The Butcher Boy

2 There is a place in that same town,
Where my love goes and sets him down,
He takes a strange girl on his knee,
And tells to her what he wouldn't tell me.

3 I went upstairs to make my bed
And nothing to my mother said;
But she followed me right up for fear
Saying, "What is the matter, daughter dear?"

4 "O mother dear, you cannot know
What pain and sorrow, grief and woe,
What pain and sorrow, grief and woe
To be in love with a butcher boy."

5 My father, when he came home that night,
Said, "Where has my dear daughter gone?"
He went upstairs and broke the door
And found her hanging by a rope.

6 He took a knife and cut her down,
And in her bosom this letter he found.
He called her mother up the stairs
And read these words through his tears:

7 "Go dig my grave, go dig it deep,
Place a marble stone at my head and feet,
And on my breast place a turtle-dove
To let the world know I died for love."

PAUL BUTTERFIELD

"WHEN the Butterfield Band came East" may well become an historical turning point in popular music. The phrase itself has almost become a commonplace one to describe the early days of folk-rock. For it was Butterfield's magic flute, in the form of a mouth harp, that helped reorient many urban folk musicians toward electric blues and a new sort of rock 'n' roll.

The harmonica of Paul Butterfield was a virtuoso vehicle, an instrument that swooped and fluttered, wailed and trumpeted, cooed and sobbed in a manner that was always musical. At its upper range it reminded many of the soprano saxophone of the late Sidney Bechet; in its other ranges it evoked cello sounds or, most arrestingly, the human voice.

Butterfield had mastered Negro urban blues style, in general, and Chicago blues, in particular, in the most authentic manner possible, by jamming with such bands as Muddy Waters'. But, of course, if exposure to influences were the only criterion, there would be many more masters than there are. Although a college-bred intellectual and former student of the classical flute, Butterfield became so immersed in Negro blues as to confound those who felt he had broken some of the rules of his birthright.

Butterfield and his band were brought East in 1965 by Paul Rothchild of Elektra Records, who had heard the band at Big John's in Chicago. He and Pete Welding of *Down Beat* were probably the two most informed fans who helped direct national attention to Paul. But once heard in New York, at the Gaslight and at the Village Gate, the Butterfield mystique needed little further touting, for a sort of spontaneous combustion took place. The knowledgeable fans and musicians had known of Muddy Waters and his brilliant harmonica player Little Walter for

years, had been struck with the easy fluency with basic blues of another white youth, John Hammond Jr., and yet found Paul perhaps even more compelling a performer. The knowledgeable fans had already moved into the camp of the Beatles, had heard and loved Chuck Berry and the electric music of Bob Dylan and the Byrds. They were ready for Paul Butterfield, and his first visit east produced a tremendous explosion of enthusiasm.

The personnel of the Butterfield Band had, of course, gone through a few changes. The biggest was the loss of its lead guitarist, Mike Bloomfield, another Chicagoan, whose instrumental technique was remarkable. In addition, the band was in flux but always maintained a mixture of Negro and white performers, for this was central to Butterfield's belief that the blues was, and should be, both interracial music and universal music.

The old blues format did not limit the emerging Butterfield Band style, and soon some elements of the psychedelic-cum-Indian sounds were incorporated. More personnel changes also ushered in a greater jazz orientation. But the band was essentially a growth group, not limited to any formula, however strong the inspiration of the blues had been.

As other modern blues bands came into existence, notably the Blues Project and the Jefferson Airplane, their obvious debt to Butterfield became apparent. Then, as the folk-rock and modern blues movement grew, one could easily have forgotten the trail-blazing efforts of Butterfield. But a turning point was marked when "the Butterfield Band came East."

213

Frankie and Johnny

Moderate Blues

Fran - kie and John - ny were lo - vers, _____ Oh Lor - dy how they could love! They swore to be true _ to each oth - er, _____ Just as true as the stars a - bove, He was her man, _____

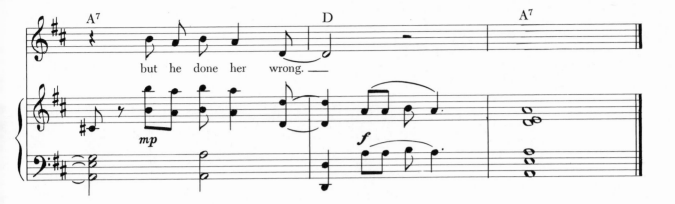

but he done her wrong. ___

2 Frankie went down to the corner,
Stopped in to buy her some beer,
She went and asked the bartender,
"Has my lovin' man been here?"
He was her man, but he done her wrong.

3 Bartender said this to Frankie:
"Ain't goin' to tell you no lie;
I saw your Johnny go upstairs
With a girl named Sally Bly."
He was her man, but he done her wrong.

4 Frankie went up the stairway,
She wasn't goin' for fun,
For in her pocket she carried
A mean ol' forty-one gun.
He was her man, but he done her wrong.

5 Johnny saw Frankie a-coming,
Out the door he did scoot,
But Frankie took aim with her pistol,
And the gun went "Root-a-toot-toot!"
He was her man, but he done her wrong.

6 "Oh roll me over so easy,
Roll me over so slow,
Roll me over easy, boys,
'Cause my wounds they hurt me so.
I was her man, but I done her wrong."

7 Drive out your rubber-tired buggy,
Drive out your rubber-tired hack;
There's eleven men going to the graveyard,
And only ten coming back.
He was her man, but he done her wrong.

215

JIM KWESKIN

AROUND the year 1963 so many jug bands were springing up across the nation that many of us thought we were on the brink of a jug-band revival in the cities that would rival the earlier Bluegrass rage.

There was an all-girl jug band at Bennington; The Even Dozen Jugband in New York; and two of the most knowledgeable blues men in the revival, Dave Van Ronk and Sam Charters, assembled another band in the East. But the revival band that started the trend and even outlasted the others was the flavorful, humorous and inventive aggregation from Cambridge, Massachusetts, led by Jim Kweskin.

The influence of the jug band has far from died out. John Sebastian carried some of its ideas over to The Lovin' Spoonful. And the latest group sensation, Spanky and Our Gang, shows similar traces of the jug phenomenon. Still, the dominant texture, instrumentation and repertoire of the jug-band revival was established and continued by Jim Kweskin's band. His band made mostly happy music, a fusion of blues, ragtime, jug-band whimsy and taut musicianship.

Jim Kweskin had been a bit of an institution around Harvard Square for some time. The singer-guitarist had a high tenor voice that commanded attention. To him Kweskin gathered Fritz Richmond, the washtub string bass player and jug player. Another strong individualist of the Kweskin band is Geoff Muldaur, a blues singer whose sobbing, intense vocalizing was one of the most distinctive sounds in the blues. Bill Keith, the gifted banjo-

picker who had worked with Bill Monroe, and Mel Lyman, on mouth harp, rounded out the band.

In the five years since its formation there have been a few personnel changes, but none more dramatic than the addition of Geoff's wife, Maria D'Amato, the charming dark-haired, button-eyed blues singer and fiddler.

This group unleashed the most diverse set of sounds imaginable, on guitar, banjo and fiddle, of course, but also on comb and tissue paper, kazoo, stovepipe, washtub bass, washboard and almost anything in sight capable of transformation into an instrument. Despite this "junkyard instrumentation," some very subtle sounds were produced. One would always listen to the Kweskin band even through the laughter they produced.

Jug-band music, in its purest and original form, was a Negro folk style that appears to have flourished around Memphis and Birmingham in the post-World War I era. It was a type of early "skiffle" music, well-suited to improvising and to unusual instruments. Early jug bands played for parties and dances and apparently provide as much fun in the 1920s as they did later in revival form in the 1960s.

When skillfully played, the jug produces a sort of wolfing tone, somewhere between the sound of a small tuba and a plucked string bass, and it can give a band a nicely propulsive rhythmic ground. But Kweskin's crew saw no need to limit themselves simply to the music of early jug bands, so they ranged off into revivals of early ragtime songs and the crooning of the "jazz age" and Depression era that followed. Although Kweskin's band used no megaphone, it was only a short hop from some of their "vo-de-do" descants to the recent interest in such bands as the New Vaudeville Band.

Jim Kweskin and his band were the first to bring forth a lot of the old sounds that keep reappearing in our pop music. They were, and are, musicians' musicians.

By and By

Fast and Strong

REFRAIN:

By and by, when the morn-ing comes,

All the saints of God are gath-ered home. We'll tell the sto - ry

how we've o-ver-come, For we'll un-der-stand it bet-ter by and by.

VERSE:

We are tossed and driv-en on the rest-less sea of time: Som-ber

skies and howl-ing temp-est oft suc - ceed a bright sun-shine; In that

land of per-fect day, when the mists have rolled a-way, We will

un-der-stand it bet-ter by and by.

2   We are often destitute of the things that life demands,
Want of shelter and of food—thirsty hills and barren lands;
We are trusting in the Lord, and according to His word,
We will understand it better by and by.

3   Trials dark on ev'ry hand, and we cannot understand
All the ways that God would lead us to that Blessed Promised Land;
But He guides us with His eye and we'll follow till we die,
For we'll understand it better by and by.

4   Temptations, hidden snares, often take us unawares,
And our hearts are made to bleed for thoughtless word or deed,
And we wonder why the test when we try to do our best;
But we'll understand it better by and by.

THERE IS a light and strength about the singing of Richie Havens that can take the listener right out of his environment, right out of his preoccupations with the here and now.

A good deal of Richie's magic is his totally individualistic approach toward rhythm. He bends it, distorts it, breaks it into little fragments, then puts the whole together. His phrases have the tension and snap of vulcanized rubber.

Richie Havens did his homework, his simmering-up, for year after year in the dumps of Greenwich Village. He told a reporter for *Newsweek* in the summer of 1967: "I feel at least 1,026 years old, but I know that's not very old." This controlled resignation on the surface may add to his underlying drive and purpose.

He was born in the second largest Negro slum of America, the Bedford-Stuyvesant section of Brooklyn, the son of a piano-playing electroplater and a mother who worked in a bindery. Home was a bit of a bindery, too, for there were nine children to feed. He got his musical exposure from a radio blaring on a Jewish station and from the store-front Negro church across the street.

As to being Negro and what it meant to him Richie said in an interview in 1967: "I don't think I ever was a Negro. I saw different colors, but, man, that seemed so small. The big question of what we are was in my head, so color meant nothing. A few people 've called me names, but it seemed funny. I'd think, man, where that cat at, he so out of it."

Richie was one of the regulars at the famous Night Owl on Third Street in Greenwich Village at the time that The Lovin' Spoonful were getting ready to go into orbit. The musicians and the very *avant-garde* fans knew it would be only a matter of time until Richie would move along toward national popularity. He recorded for Verve/Forecast and slowly, deliberately he built his audience.

Appearances at the Fillmore East and the Fillmore West, Bill Graham's dual clubs and concert halls, really helped establish him with the rock-pop-folk *avant-garde*. After all the groups that had soared and shouted with electric energy and blare, to hear Havens doing his alternately introverted or dancing songs was a contrast but never a letdown.

Here was a stylist who never quite left a song the way he had found it. Here was an individualist who put his own mark on everything he sang, from Dylan songs to his own works. At the massive tribute to Woody Guthrie that took place in Carnegie Hall, Richie Havens was a proud part. He was the "newest" of the performers and, with the exception of Arlo Guthrie, the "youngest." Richie belonged, as an important newcomer has a way of belonging. He belongs by virtue of a powerful talent.

RICHIE HAVENS

The Lily of the West

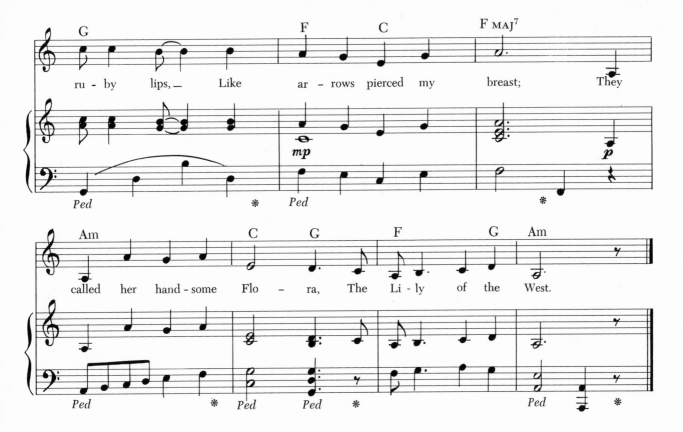

2 I courted her for many a day,
I thought her love to gain.
Too soon, too soon she slighted me,
Which caused me grief and pain.
She robbed me of my liberty,
Deprived me of my rest;
But still I loved my Flora,
The Lily of the West.

3 As I walked out one evening
Down in yon shady grove,
I saw a lord of high degree
Conversing with my love.
He sang, he sang so merrily,
While I was sore distressed;
He sang for handsome Flora,
The Lily of the West.

4 I rushed up to my rival
A dagger in my hand,
I caught him by the collar
And boldly bade him stand.
Being mad to desperation,
My dagger pierced his breast.
I was betrayed by Flora,
The Lily of the West.

5 And now my trial has come off
And sentenced soon I'll be.
They put me in the criminal box
And there convicted me.
She so deceived the jury,
So modestly did dress,
She far outshone bright Venus,
The Lily of the West.

6 Since then I've gained my liberty,
I'll roam the country through,
I'll travel the cities over
To find my loved one true.
Though she robbed me of my liberty,
Deprived me of my rest,
But still I love my Flora,
The Lily of the West.

SIMON AND GARFUNKEL

THE FOLK movement has, in the last decade, run up a long and distinguished list of discoveries, whether from rural obscurity or earnest city youth. But somehow or other the folk scene was asleep while one of the most important pair of stars was germinating.

Despite this omission, Paul Simon and Arthur Garfunkel have ultimately prospered. In the last two years these New York boys have garnered international renown and an audience that cuts across all age and stylistic boundaries.

Perhaps the folk fans just weren't ready for Simon and Garfunkel in their early appearances at Folk City and the Gaslight in Greenwich Village. The then ethnic-oriented audience possibly couldn't quite cope with the polish and finesse that Paul and Artie brought to Paul's growing repertoire of stunning songs. Then, too, Paul and Arthur had been spending a good deal of time in Britain and were actually "prophets without honor in their own land" when success came.

It did come in the most unusual way. Their recording of "Sounds of Silence" had, unbeknownst to them, been overdubbed with studio rhythm added and emerged as a chart hit. However unorthodox this advent to popularity was, it opened the door for a whole series of thoughtful, perceptive songs by Simon, including "Dangling Conversation," "I Am a Rock" and many more.

Simon and Garfunkel have elevated the urban topical "message" song a few rungs up the ladder with artfulness, economy and refinement. They have stretched the limit of the folk-rock song to include such universal and compelling questions as communication, alienation, loneliness and the quest for workable ethics in an increasingly problematic society.

Musically, their distinctiveness lies in their finely honed close harmony whose caressing qualities some commentators have likened to church harmo-

nies. They are the first performers of their kind to make a giant impact on Hollywood with their songs and singing in the vastly successful movie *The Graduate*.

Paul and Arthur were high-school friends in Forest Hills, Queens, when they began to sing together. In an older pop vein, under the names Tom and Jerry, they had an early small hit with "Hey, Schoolgirl." Paul studied literature at Queens College, did some song-plugging and record-producing for various labels, left law school in disinterest and began to sing in England. Arthur, somehow, has managed a full academic career while singing at weekend college concerts with Paul. Arthur received a master's degree in mathematics in early 1966 and is hard at work on a Ph.D. as he is arranging and singing the duo's next Columbia record.

Simon and Garfunkel are a close collaborative effort. To Paul's music and lyrics Arthur is the strong, silent editor and arranger. Having already lasted nearly a decade, their team approach is considered one of the most harmonious in the entire folk and pop group scene.

As their favored traditional folk song, Paul and Arthur have chosen the old English air "Scarborough Fair." This lovely folk lyric was collected in the last century in Somerset, in the west of England. They have recorded it in a modernized treatment interwoven with "Canticle" on their album "Parsley, Sage, Rosemary and Thyme." It also became a best-selling single. In that version and this, one is struck by the durability of the best classic folk songs.

222

Scarborough Fair

Moderately Fast

VERSE:

"Oh, where are you go - ing?" "To Scar - bo - rough Fair,"

Pars - ley, sage, — rose - ma - ry and thyme, "Re - mem - ber me to

one who lives there, For once she was — a true love of mine."

2 "Tell her to make me a cambric shirt,"
Parsley, sage, rosemary, and thyme;
"Without any seam or needlework,
For once she was a true love of mine.

3 "Tell her to wash it in yonder well,"
Parsley, sage, rosemary, and thyme;
"Where never spring water nor rain ever fell,
For once she was a true love of mine.

223

4   "Tell her to dry it on yonder thorn,"
Parsley, sage, rosemary, and thyme;
"Which never bore blossom since Adam was born,
For once she was a true love of mine."

5   "Now he has asked me questions three,"
Parsley, sage, rosemary, and thyme;
"I hope he will answer as many for me,
For once he was a true love of mine.

6   "Tell him to find me an acre of land,"
Parsley, sage, rosemary, and thyme;
"Betwixt the salt water and the sea sand,
For once he was a true love of mine.

7   "Tell him to plough it with a ram's horn,"
Parsley, sage, rosemary, and thyme;
"And sow it all over with one pepper corn,
For once he was a true love of mine.

8   "Tell him to reap it with a sickle of leather,"
Parsley, sage, rosemary, and thyme;
"And bind it up with a peacock's feather,
For once he was a true love of mine.

9   "When he has done and finished his work,"
Parsley, sage, rosemary, and thyme;
"O tell him to come and he'll have his shirt,
For once he was a true love of mine."

A FEW DOUR observers of the folk scene were taking the glum attitude in the middle 1960s that all was over, that the revival had ended. Worse than that, they feared that the pop, rock and country music worlds were siphoning off all the new, fresh talent.

Into this gloomy atmosphere shone a new, gifted singer-songwriter, a product of the urban folk movement, a philosopher at the age of only sixteen: Janis Ian. Although she recorded with pop and electric backing, Janis was the city minstrel sort, appearing in public with just her guitar and her arsenal of tough-minded, compelling songs.

"Society's Child" was the best-known of these protest songs, an economical and yet moving narrative that summed up many deep feelings about the racial issue. In the song, a white girl, who has been dating a Negro boy, breaks off the relationship, lamenting the bias of parents, her teachers, her classmates and, finally, her own weakness to rise above the strictures that surround any "society's child."

The song, understandably, had a stormy history. After it was independently recorded by George (Shadow) Morton, all the big record companies shied away from it. Finally, Jerry Schoenbaum, an executive of Verve-Folkways Records, decided to accept the challenge of controversy and even to capitalize on it. After sporadic air play and a ripple of interest, the song died an early death. A few people, notably Murray (the K) Kaufman, Robert Shelton and Richard Goldstein, tried to make an issue over the song, but to little avail. Then Leonard Bernstein, conductor of the New York Philharmonic, decided to single out Janis and "Society's Child" on a CBS-TV pop-musical special. It became an overnight hit, some nine months after its release.

Then, all of a sudden, Janis became "public domain," and everyone was tuning in on her and her other songs. Most of them were cast in the mold of "generational" message songs, talking to teens and to parents of teens about the gulf of understanding, compassion and communication that had grown between them. In such a vein were "Younger Generation Blues" and "Janey's Blues."

But, as with Simon and Garfunkel and other latter-day "message singers," Janis was building on the past of Dylan, Seeger, Ochs and Paxton, showing considerable musical polish and inventiveness, coupled with skillfully wrought words. Here was no simple sloganeer but a deft spokeswoman, amazingly only sixteen, who could cope with problems of being a teenager in America today.

Janis is the product of a musical home, her father having been a music teacher and a camp director. Outside her home, the greatest stimulus came from *New York Broadside Magazine*. Her first major exposure had been at a *Broadside* hootenanny at the Village Gate when Janis was only fourteen. She was also very much a product of the New York intellectual climate, a student at the famed High School of Music and Art.

It is difficult to predict trends in either folk song or pop song, because they may change quite quickly. But clearly, Janis Ian and her "generation music" is one path that certainly points toward the future. And her emergence to national popularity should give heart to any of those who feared the decline in folk song, or topical song, or the solo singer-songwriter working with guitar.

Janis' choice is obviously not a traditional song, but it is so appropriate to her and to this collection that we are including it. "God Bless' the Child" is one of the great classics of American music, and to Janis as the youngest artist included in this collection we say, "God Bless the Child who's got his own."

JANIS IAN

A swing-spiritual based on the authentic proverb
"God blessed the child that's got his own."

God Bless' the Child

226

Words and Music by Arthur Herzog, Jr. and Billie Holiday
Copyright 1941 by Edward B. Marks Music Corporation.
All rights reserved. Used by permission.

When you're gone and spend-ing ends,— They don't come no more. Rich re-la-tions give, Crust of bread, and such, You can help your-self, But don't take too much! Ma-ma may have, Pa-pa may have, But God bless' the child that's got his own! That's got his own.

ARLO GUTHRIE

IF YOU haven't heard about Alice's Restaurant by now, kid, you're in trouble. Well, maybe not trouble, but you sure have missed out on one of the great story-songs or song-stories of our time. Oh, yes, kid, it was written and sung and recorded by Arlo Guthrie.

The Newport Folk Festival of 1967 was the one that turned the trick for Arlo. Every festival in Rhode Island seems to find a need for some special event, some new hero or song to latch onto. In 1967, the passion was for Arlo Guthrie and "Alice's Restaurant Massacree." Said John S. Wilson of *The New York Times*: "Mr. Guthrie's delivery was so wry and dry, his timing so keenly calculated and the simple tune so maddeningly memorable that it captivated one audience after another. . . ."

To a writer from *The New Yorker*, Arlo "looked six or seven years younger than twenty—his face long and childish (a sort of Skeezix drawn by Modigliani). . . ." He is full of talent, his own and that inherited from his illustrious father, Woody. For a time, a difficult time while Arlo was trying to find his own place in the world, he talked little of Woody. Then, just the year that the father died, the son "arrived" and there was a family again.

Arlo's magnificent sense of humor and timing, his wry view of the world make him a joy to watch and hear. His thoughtfulness make him a person to listen to. Altogether, here is an important new artist.

Arlo is the oldest child of Woody's marriage to Marjorie Mazia Guthrie. Naturally, the great figure of Woody Guthrie filled Arlo's early years. His first sing-song in public, he recalls, was with the late Cisco Houston at Gerde's Folk City in New York when Arlo was only about ten years old.

After Marjorie, the first to recognize Arlo's rare talent was Woody's longtime friend and manager, Harold Leventhal. It is fortunate that Arlo's career is being supervised by Leventhal, who, in addition to his insight into and knowledge of music and entertainment, has himself developed into a "giant" by virtue of his integrity and courage. His gentle and careful handling of Arlo, plus the musical supervision and record production of Fred Hellerman, assure us that Arlo's potential will be developed with taste and skill.

In a rare and charming bit of prose, on the liner to Arlo's Reprise album, Harold wrote: "The fact of the matter is that this chain of events was inevitable. I have known the Guthrie family for a good number of years and first knew Arlo when he was about four years old, living with his parents. . . . Music was as natural to Arlo's household as the bed he slept in. From the very beginning, Arlo was learning from the best. . . ."

Arlo moved to Stockbridge, Massachusetts, the town in the Berkshires that has a place very much like Alice's Restaurant. When he is not touring now, from England to New England, Arlo holes up there in the countryside. He writes songs there, and sings them, and turns his devilishly clever mind to all sorts of new things. We all remember Arlo when he was a kid calling everyone kid, but he's a big boy now.

Old McDonald Had a Farm

Old Mc Don - ald had a farm,— E - I - E - I - O, And on this farm he had some (1) chicks, E - I - E - I - O. With a
(2) pigs a an
(3) ducks a
(4) cows a

*(Repeat for each verse except the 1st. Sing each preceding verse until
the 1st verse, then proceed to CODA)*

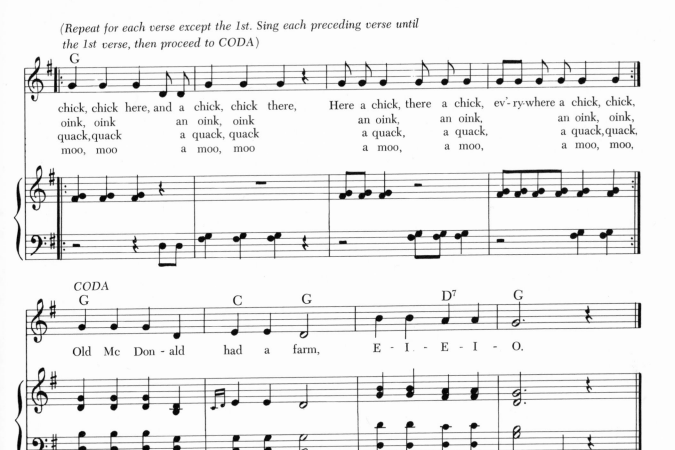

chick, chick here, and a chick, chick there,   Here a chick, there a chick, ev'-ry-where a chick, chick,
oink, oink   an oink, oink,   an oink,   an oink,   an oink, oink,
quack, quack   a quack, quack   a quack,   a quack,   a quack, quack,
moo, moo   a moo, moo   a moo,   a moo,   a moo, moo,

CODA

Old Mc Don - ald had a farm, E - I - E - I - O.

David's Lamentation

Words and Music by William Billings
Harmonization and arrangement by Milton Okun

233

PHOTO CREDITS

Artist	*Photographed by*
Tom Smothers	Mort Shuman
The Kingston Trio	Baron Wolman Photography
The New Lost City Ramblers	Robert Frank
Josh White	Bengt Ohlson
Jean Ritchie	George Pickow
Reverend Gary Davis	Leonard Schechter
Merle Travis	Capitol Records, Inc.
Mississippi John Hurt	David Gahr
Muddy Waters	Bettye Lane
Joan Baez	Gaveau
Malvina Reynolds	Eleanor M. Lawrence
Doc Watson	Dan Seeger
Mahalia Jackson	Columbia Records Photo
Johnny Cash	Columbia Records Photo

Index

Songs printed in this book are in bold type;
first lines of songs are within quotation marks;
italics indicate song titles mentioned in the book.